SIMULATION TECHNIQUES FOR DESIGN

OF WATER–RESOURCE SYSTEMS

SIMULATION TECHNIQUES FOR DESIGN OF WATER–RESOURCE SYSTEMS

MAYNARD M. HUFSCHMIDT

MYRON B FIERING

HARVARD UNIVERSITY PRESS   CAMBRIDGE, MASSACHUSETTS   1966

PREFACE

This book is a guide for constructing simulation models for water-resource systems. It presents the various steps and procedures required to institute a simulation program, including procedures for collecting and organizing hydrologic and economic data, and for developing the logic and detailed computer code for the simulation program. In addition, the book contains a detailed report on application of these steps and procedures to constructing a simulation program for a specific water-resource system—the Lehigh River basin in Pennsylvania. While the book is not intended to serve as a manual of *detailed* procedure, it provides general guidelines, much specific information, and many examples which should be useful to planning organizations that may wish to develop suitable manuals of procedure for their own use. The book should also serve as an aid in teaching the use of simulation in water-resource planning.

The role of simulation in water-resource system design can be described by defining its place in the methodology of planning developed by the Harvard Water Program, and reported in A. Maass, M. Hufschmidt, R. Dorfman, H. A. Thomas, Jr., S. Marglin, and G. M. Fair, *Design of Water-Resource Systems*, Harvard University Press, 1962. This methodology consists of four sequential steps:

(1) specifying the *objectives* of design;

(2) translating the objectives into *design criteria;*

(3) using the design criteria to formulate *specific designs* for development and management of water-resource systems that fulfill the objectives to the highest degree; and

(4) evaluating the *consequences* of these designs.

The third step includes all of the studies and analyses required to prepare at field level a regional or river-basin plan—or, as it is called in this book, a water-resource system design. The major elements of this design task are:

(1) collection and analysis of basic data on present and projected *demand* for resources, including studies of population, economic activity, and demand schedules for water-derived goods and services;

(2) collection and analysis of basic data on resource *supply*, including studies of climate, soil, topography, geology, and hydrology;

(3) assembly of an inventory of development and management alternatives, including possible dams, reservoirs, irrigation works, power plants, flood-damage alleviation measures, and the like;

(4) preliminary screening of alternatives in a systems context, to identify those promising measures suitable for further analysis; and

(5) detailed analyses of systems of such alternatives leading to identification of an optimal design or designs.

Techniques of systems analysis appropriate for the preliminary screening and the detailed analysis have been studied intensively by the Harvard Water Program. These techniques fall into two classes: (i) analytical models and (ii) simulation models. Each class is concerned with analysis of systems; each aspires to optimization; and each relies heavily for its utility as a design tool on the digital computer. Each class also has its own appropriate role in solving practical problems of water-resource system design; this book is concerned with the suitability of simulation for this purpose.

Our approach has been to apply simulation to an actual planning problem — in this case, the preparation of a water-resource investment plan for the Lehigh River basin — and to extend the technique to simulation of a much larger system — the entire Delaware River basin. From these exercises it has been possible to assess the performance of simulation as a means of analyzing alternative water-resource system designs and to perceive the advantages and limitations of using the technique.

The theory underlying the recommended procedure is not presented in detail; instead, citations are given to appropriate sections of *Design of Water-Resource Systems* and other relevant literature.

Thus, we sketch only the general outlines of the statistical theory which buttresses the hydrologic analysis and the generation of operational (synthetic) hydrology. Nor have we attempted to explain the theory of welfare economics which supports the cost and benefit functions and the economic analysis used in the simulation model.

The Lehigh basin simulation model and associated computer programs were developed for a planning problem concerned with surface-water alone and with four purposes — water supply, hydroelectric power, flood-damage alleviation, and recreation. Although detailed treatment of other important aspects of water-resource planning is absent, major segments of the analysis are broadly applicable to other purposes such as irrigation, navigation, water-quality management, and fish and wildlife management. Appropriate references are given to other studies dealing with purposes not covered here in detail.

With minor exceptions, cost and benefit data used in the Lehigh simulation model are taken from the report of the Corps of Engineers on the Delaware River basin (H. Doc. 87–522). The form and method of constructing cost and benefit functions described in the book are generally applicable to other river systems; only the numbers will be different.

Flow charts for selected subroutines of the Lehigh and Delaware programs are included. The complete source program and supporting documentation are not presented because they can be of little direct use in simulation of other river systems. But the descriptions given should enable the engineer, planner, and computer programmer to adapt simulation to other cases.

The research reported here was conducted during the four-year period, 1961–1965, with primary support from the U.S. Army Corps of Engineers under a contract with the Harvard Water Program in the Graduate School of Public Administration. Supplementary support was given by the U.S. Public Health Service and Resources for the Future, Inc.

The book is a joint product of the authors in the sense that together they drafted and edited the final manuscript. Each author, however, had major responsibility for initial preparation of specific sections, consistent with his area of specialization. Myron Fiering wrote the section in Chapter 2 on organizing and analyzing hydrologic data, and all of Chapter 3 on the Lehigh Simulation Program. Maynard Hufschmidt wrote the remainder of Chapter 2, Organizing for Simulation. In this he was assisted by John Wilkinson. Chapter 5, relating to the extension of the simulation technique to the Delaware basin, was prepared initially by Raphael Zahler who, using the Lehigh as a model, coded the entire Delaware River system for simulation on the digital computer.

Special acknowledgments are due to John Wilkinson for his substantial contribution to the work, especially in the preparation and analysis of data on cost and benefit functions, and to Sheldon Rosenberg for his meticulously accurate work on preparing streamflow data and his service as a programming aide. Arthur Maass read the entire manuscript in draft and made many valuable suggestions for improvement. The manuscript was reviewed in draft by water-resource planners in the Corps of Engineers and many useful suggestions were received. Others who commented on specific portions were Blair Bower, Robert Kates, and Allen Kneese.

Special thanks are due to Miss Ellen Munson and Mrs. Marian Adams who typed the numerous drafts; to Mrs. Lesley Mooney who served as a programming assistant, and to Elmer Rising and William Minty who prepared the drawings. All of the computations were performed on the IBM 7094 System at the Harvard Computing Center, whose expert staff merit our thanks.

Sponsorship of the research by the U.S. Army Corps of Engineers implies no commitment by that agency to the substance and findings of this book.

M. M. H.
M. B F.

CONTENTS

LIST OF TABLES   xiii

LIST OF GRAPHS   xv

1 INTRODUCTION   1

2 ORGANIZING FOR SIMULATION OF A
WATER–RESOURCE SYSTEM   4

Defining the System   4

Organizing and Analyzing Streamflow Data   14

System Design Variables, Parameters, and Constants   29

Establishing an Operating Procedure   40

Constructing Cost and Benefit Functions   42

Benefit Functions   54

    Economic-loss Functions   77

Arranging for Summary Economic Analyses   82

    I. Static Analysis   84

    II. Dynamic Analysis   85

Summary   88

3 THE LEHIGH SIMULATION PROGRAM   89

The EXECUTIVE Routines   93

    MAIN Program   93

      Subroutine SETUP   94

      Subroutine SETUPB   95

      Subroutine READ 1   95

      Subroutine READ2   95

    The Hydrology Algorithm   95

      Subroutine SYNHYD   96

    The Monthly Algorithm in Detail   96

      A. Basic Policy   96

B. The Subroutines in Detail   98
    Subroutine BASIC   99
    Subroutine POWER   99
    Subroutine DIVERT   106
    Subroutine WATER   109
    Subroutine SUPPOW   110
    Subroutine SPACE   117
The Flood Algorithm   125
    General Statement   125
    Subroutine FGEN   125
    Subroutine HYDRO   129
    Subroutine ROUTER   130
    Subroutine FSPACE   132
Benefit and Cost Analyses   133
    The Monthly Benefit Algorithm (Subroutine BENACM)   133
    The Annual Benefit Algorithm (Subroutine BENACY)   135
    The Run Benefit Algorithm   136
    Subroutine BENDYN   136
    Subroutine COST   137
The Output Algorithm   138
Service Routines   139
    Subroutine GM   139
    Subroutine RANDM   151

4 VALIDATION AND APPLICATION OF THE PROGRAM   152
Validation   152
    The Presence of Blunders   152
    Internal Inconsistencies   153
    Consistency of Generated and Observed Hydrologic Values 154
    Necessity and Sufficiency   154
    Acceptance of the Streamflow Generator   154
    Measures of Risk Aversion   156
Application of the Model   158
    Strategy   158
    Results   159

5 EXTENSION OF THE LEHIGH BASIN MODEL: THE
   DELAWARE BASIN SIMULATION MODEL   171
Introduction   171
Outline of the Simulation Procedure   171

The Subroutines in Detail   174
   The Monthly Operating Algorithm   174
      Subroutine BOX   176
      Subroutine SPACE   177
      Subroutine BASIC   181
      Subroutine MONT   181
      Subroutine WATER   183
      Subroutine POWER   184
   The Benefit Algorithm   186
      Subroutine SETUPB   186
      Subroutine BENACM   186
      Subroutine BENACY   187
      Subroutine BENDYN   188
      Subroutine COST   188
   The Input–Output Algorithm   189
      Subroutine READ1   189
      Subroutine WRITE1   189
      Subroutine WRITE2   189
   The Flood Algorithm   190
Concluding Comments   190

6 LESSONS AND PROSPECTS   193
  Man   193
  Machine   194
  Flexibility of the Program   196
  Prospects for Application   197

  APPENDIX I   203

  APPENDIX II   205

  INDEX   207

TABLES

2.1 Cases for Lehigh system designs, with associated reservoir and turbine numbers and power plant locations. 12

2.2 Drainage area relationships between gaging stations and dam sites, Lehigh River system. 25

2.3 Periods of streamflow records used in hydrologic analyses of the Lehigh River system. 26

2.4 Means and standard deviations (10^3 acre ft) of monthly streamflows, Lehigh River basin, from historical record. 28

2.5 Major physical design variables, Lehigh system. 31

2.6 Monthly percentages of annual target outputs for water supply and energy. 35

2.7 Monthly distribution of annual recreation attendance (percent), Lehigh River basin. 68

3.1 Output block. 140

4.1 Summary of costs and benefits; random sample of 20 designs. 160

4.2 Summary of costs and benefits; systematic sample of eight designs, using design no. 16 of random sample as the base. 162

4.3 Systematic sample of four designs, using design no. 20 of random sample as the base. 164

4.4 Systematic sample of three designs, using design no. 18 of random sample as the base. 166

4.5 Benefits and flood damages (in 10^6 dollars) for five demand periods and entire period of economic analysis for the base design (no. 9, Table 4.2), with three different hydrologic traces. 167

4.6 Benefits for the base design, undiscounted and discounted simulation runs; for synthetic trace and trace of actual hydrology. 169

GRAPHS

2.1 Defining a water-resource system for simulation. The supply configuration for a sample basin.   6

2.2 Defining a water-resource system for simulation. The supply configuration for the Lehigh basin example.   8

2.3 Defining a water-resource system for simulation. Water demands and problems for a sample basin.   8

2.4 Defining a water-resource system for simulation. Water demands and problems for the Lehigh basin example.   9

2.5 Defining a water-resource system for simulation. Development measures for a sample basin.   10

2.6 Defining a water-resource system for simulation. Development measures for the Lehigh basin example.   11

2.7 Parameters for synthesis of flood hydrographs. Simple model adopted for Lehigh simulation program.   21

2.8 Parameters for synthesis of flood hydrographs. First version of model devised for use in the Lehigh simulation program.   22

2.9 Capacity of diversion tunnel from Lehigh River to reservoir 3 as a function of capacity of reservoir 3.   33

2.10 Head and reservoir contents at reservoirs 1–6.   37

2.11 Schematic diagram of reservoirs 1, 2, and 4, and Beltzville pipe.   38

2.12 Schematic diagram of reservoir 2 and Lehigh pipe.   38

2.13 Capital costs of reservoirs 1, 2, and 3.   44

2.14 Capital costs of reservoirs 4, 5, and 6.   44

2.15 Unit capital cost of hydroelectric power plant as a function of gross head, for units of various sizes.   47

2.16 Unit capital cost of penstock, power plants 1–6.   47

2.17 Unit capital cost of auxiliary power facilities, reservoirs 1 and 2, power plants 7 and 8 (Beltzville pipe).   49

2.18 Unit capital cost of auxiliary power facilities, reservoir 1, power plant 9 (Lehigh pipe).   49

2.19 Unit annual recreation attendance as a function of reservoir capacity, reservoirs 1–6.   51

2.20 Annual OMR cost as a function of capital cost, reservoirs 1–6.   53

2.21 Annual OMR cost, power plants 1–9.   54

2.22 Two-element benefit function: element A shows benefits as a function of target output per unit time; element B_1-B_2 shows benefits as a function of attained outputs when target output is $\bar{x}$.   55

2.23 Aggregate demand function for domestic and industrial
     water supply.   58
2.24 Benefit functions for domestic and industrial water supply.   59
2.25 Unit firm hydroelectric power benefits and hydroelectric
     plant capacity factor for various interest rates, using the
     cost of external alternative (thermal plant) as a measure of
     benefits.   64
2.26 Benefit function for firm hydroelectric power using the al-
     ternative cost measure with discount rate of 2.5 percent
     and plant factor of 20 percent.   65
2.27 Gross irrigation benefit function.   69
2.28 Derivation of flood damage–discharge function from stage-
     discharge and flood damage-stage functions.   70
2.29 Flood damage–discharge functions based on alternative
     management assumptions.   73
2.30 Flood damage–discharge function, Bethlehem–Allentown
     zones, Lehigh River system.   74
2.31 Flood damage–discharge functions, Aquashicola Creek and
     Walnutport zones, Lehigh River system.   74
2.32 Flood damage–discharge functions, Jordan Creek and Po-
     hopoco Creek zones, Lehigh River system.   75
2.33 Unit water-supply loss functions, Lehigh River system,
     under various assumptions of severity of loss. Losses over
     50 percent of monthly target are valued at 10^5 dollars per
     10^2 acre ft.   78
2.34 Energy-loss function. Deficits in excess of 25 percent of
     monthly target are penalized at 10^3 dollars per kwhr.   79
2.35 Recreation loss functions, Lehigh River system, under va-
     rious assumptions of severity of loss.   81
2.36 Time profile of system benefits for dynamic analysis with
     benefits discounted as stream of equal annual values.   87
3.1 General flow chart of the Lehigh simulation program.   91
3.2 Calling sequence of subroutines in the Monthly Algorithm.   98
3.3 Flow chart for subroutine BASIC.   100
3.4 Flow chart for subroutine POWER.   102
3.5 Flow chart for subroutine DIVERT.   106
3.6 Flow chart for subroutine WATER.   108
3.7 Flow chart for subroutine SUPPOW.   112
3.8 Flow chart for subroutine SPACE.   118
3.9 Form of synthetic flood hydrograph generated by subrou-
     tine FGEN.   126
5.1 Schematic diagram of Delaware River system.   172
5.2 Flow chart for EXECUTIVE routine.   173
5.3 Flow chart for subroutine BOX.   177
5.4 Flow chart for subroutine SPACE.   178
5.5 Flow chart for subroutine MONT.   182
6.1 Storage-yield contours at several levels of reliability.   199

SIMULATION TECHNIQUES FOR DESIGN

OF WATER–RESOURCE SYSTEMS

1 INTRODUCTION

Simulation as a technique for analyzing the behavior of physical systems has a long history, but only in recent years has its use become widespread as a tool for problem-solving. This has come about as part of the rapid development of operations research and systems analysis and associated advances in electronic computers.

In general terms, simulation is a process which "duplicate[s] the essence of a system or activity without actually attaining reality itself." [1] Admittedly, this is a broad definition. It encompasses analog and digital simulations, physical devices such as hydraulic models and training machines (for pilots and automobile drivers), models strategic of defense systems, industrial and business operations, water-resource and transportation systems, and entire regional and national economies.

Planners turn to simulation because it is often the only method for dealing effectively with large and complex problems that defy analytical solution or that cannot be reproduced by experiment on actual systems. [2] The design of water-resource systems supplies striking examples of such intractable systems. The difficulties arise from the complex relationships and interdependencies among the design variables (dams, power plants, target outputs for water supply, power, and the like) and the hydrology. Also, data on the behavior of actual water-resource systems (such as the TVA system) cannot be fully extrapolated to obtain useful predictions of the behavior of systems still under design.

It is not surprising, therefore, that water-resource planners and hydraulic engineers use simulation methods to help in design. One

[1] R. L. Ackoff, *Progress in operations research* (John Wiley, New York, 1961), p. 367.

[2] For a discussion of the rationale of simulation, see Ackoff, reference 1, pp. 366, 372, and R. Dorfman, "Operations Research," *AER, 50,* 603 (1960).

aspect of simulation that has found effective use in hydraulic problems is the physical model—represented by an analog of a harbor, an estuary, a dam and reservoir, or an entire river system—scaled to maintain static or dynamic similitude.[3] Closely related to these models are electric analogs which express all relationships and results in terms of appropriately scaled continuous electrical units (volts, amperes, ohms).

Finally, digital, or symbolic, simulation for solution of hydraulic and hydrologic problems is a well-established tool. The model accounts for flows of water in an assumed system of dams, control works, and use points during a specified sequence of time increments. These system operating studies often evaluate performance over a period of several years of critical low flows, usually derived from actual records of streamflow. In addition, special operating studies are made for estimating the effects of control works on flood flows or on critical low flows over shorter time spans—days or weeks.

Until electronic computers became generally available, digital simulation studies were so time-consuming as to be of limited use in system design. Typically, a few alternative plans were checked in the final stages of design by making a simulation or operation study covering the few years of critical low flow, but no attempts were made to simulate the performance of a large number of alternative designs; nor were simulations extended to handle time periods as long as the selected periods of economic analysis.

Water-resource planning agencies first began to use the digital computer to perform the same kinds of simulation that were amenable to desk calculator manipulation; they found it possible to make many more and longer simulation analyses than previously. In fact, most computer simulations of water-resource systems performed over the past ten years are of this type.

These conventional simulations suffer from two disadvantages: (1) By testing system performance with only a single hydrologic sequence—obtained from the actual record of streamflows—only a single estimate of performance is obtained; no information is gained on the response to other, equally likely, patterns of flow,

---

[3] The Vicksburg, Mississippi, laboratories of the U.S. Army Corps of Engineers and the Denver, Colorado, laboratories of the U.S. Bureau of Reclamation contain many such models.

and thus nothing can be inferred about the statistical distribution of system responses to potential hydrologic patterns. (2) By focusing primarily on physical performance (magnitude and persistence of deficits, for example), evaluation in economic terms is underemphasized and design decisions are likely to be based on inadequate economic analysis.

The simulation analyses described in this book are more advanced than conventional water-resource simulations; they avoid many of the shortcomings of the older methods. Rather than evaluating the performance of only a few designs, our simulation program is equipped to deal with a large number of alternative designs. The sizes of structures and levels of target outputs are input variables and can be arranged in many different combinations. Our method includes the generation of long hydrologic sequences for testing the performance of alternative designs, and measures outcomes in economic terms. System costs and benefits, including economic losses arising from output deficits, are computed, and results are summarized in terms of net benefits — gross benefits less costs — under a variety of assumptions as to interest rates and schedules of development.[4]

Chapters 2 and 3 illustrate the application of these methods to an actual case — the Lehigh River system — and thereby provide information on how basic data might be arranged and the simulation program organized to achieve the desired results. Chapter 4 deals with problems of validating the simulation model and presents the results of applying the model to testing alternative designs for the Lehigh River system. Chapter 5 reports on the extension of the simulation technique developed for the Lehigh to the much larger Delaware River system. General findings and conclusions are presented in the concluding chapter. Glossaries of FORTRAN symbols used in the text and flow charts are contained in the appendices.

[4] Simulation analyses of the Columbia River system by the North Pacific Division, U.S. Army Corps of Engineers, represent the most advanced applications to actual systems in this country. Current programs are capable of handling actual and synthetic flow sequences, and testing many alternative system designs; the programs also allow considerable flexibility in operating policy. See D. J. Lewis and L. A. Shoemaker, "Hydro system power analysis by digital computer," *Trans. Am. Soc. Civil Engrs.*, 128-1, *1074* (1963). An advanced simulation of a hydroelectric system in Canada is reported by J. Borbeau, F. Jonker, and J. Thomson, "Economic development of Hydro-Quebec power resources," *Engin. J.* October 1961.

2 ORGANIZING FOR SIMULATION OF A WATER-RESOURCE SYSTEM

Arranging for digital computer simulation of a water-resource system is far from simple, even for a system with few variables. And in the typical case, with multiple uses and structures and with complicated water-flow and use patterns, the task attains formidable proportions. It is important, therefore, that preparation of data in forms appropriate for simulation coding be carefully organized.

In this chapter the problem of organizing a simulation study in general terms and in terms of application to a particular case — the Lehigh River system — is presented in the following sequence:

(a) defining the system and establishing its configuration, including the network of surface and ground-water flows and the points of water use and control;

(b) manipulating the hydrologic data in forms appropriate for use in simulation, including establishing a procedure for synthesizing hydrologic events;

(c) defining the system design variables and physical parameters and constants;

(d) establishing an operating procedure for the system;

(e) evaluating costs and benefits associated with the design variables and outputs; and

(f) evaluating economic consequences of system designs under several assumed interest rates, static and dynamic investment patterns, and methods of discounting benefits and costs.

DEFINING THE SYSTEM

At first glance the initial step — defining the system — appears so obvious as to require no elaboration. One has a picture of a river system, with points of water use (municipalities, irrigable lands) and water control (existing or potential) clearly identified. Defining the system, therefore, would seem to imply merely a schematic map showing the main stream(s) and tributaries and the points of water use and control. Indeed, such a map is an essential part of the definition of the system, but, in general, it will be the end-product of a detailed analysis of the planning area and its physical and economic characteristics as related to water use and control. For example, the boundaries of the system are not necessarily coterminous with river basin boundaries, but may extend beyond, to take account of surface–ground–water relationships and extra-basin demands for water, hydroelectric power, or recreation.

Fortunately, much prior analysis, including definition of the appropriate planning area, will have been undertaken in the early stages of water-resource planning. Once the planning area is defined, it is the general practice to apply preliminary screening techniques to reduce the number of alternative combinations of development measures and water uses to those likely to be most productive.[1] In the general case, the number of alternatives subject to screening techniques may be very large; in the Lehigh simulation example, the combination of six storage reservoirs, nine power plants, and four uses emerges as the product of prior analysis of a somewhat larger number of potentially productive alternatives.

A convenient method of classifying the many elements which comprise a water-resource system is to distinguish among those involving (1) the *supply* of water; (2) the *demand* for water-derived products and services; and (3) the *development measures* for adjusting, temporally and spatially, the supply to the demand.

Supply. Major elements of supply are the vectors of surface and ground water flows and natural storage. The relevant characteristics of supply are quantity, quality, and availability measured with respect to time and location. Typically, ground water under or adjacent to flowing streams contributes to surface flow during periods of low surface runoff and is replenished when surface flow is ample, but the relationship of ground to surface water is quite different where ground-water basins are supplied from distant surface flows. A ground-water aquifer may lie in a different river

[1] See, for example, *Report on Delaware River basin, New York, New Jersey, Pennsylvania and Delaware*, House Doc. 522, 87 Cong., vol. IX, Appendix Q; and U.S. Army Engineer District, Baltimore, *Potomac River basin report* (February 1963) vol. I, chap. 8. See also M. M. Hufschmidt, "Field-level planning of water-resource systems," *Journal of Water Resources Research, 1*, 147 (May 1965).

system from its zone of recharge; in this case, ground-water flows represent an export of water from the recharging basin. Whatever their form, all significant surface–ground–water relationships should be identified, and measures of their magnitude obtained where possible. Land-water relationships, including erosion, siltation, and evaporation characteristics for various segments of the river system must also be identified and measured in quantitative terms; and the degree of salinization or other mineralization of water arising from natural causes must be established.

Figure 2.1 shows a set of relationships associated with the supply vectors. Because only a general definition of the system is desired at this stage of the simulation study, no attempt is made to attach numerical values to the several supply vectors; accordingly, magnitudes of surface or ground-water flows, siltation, evaporation, or salinization rates are not given. It is enough to establish that significant relationships exist and to define, as well as possible, their location and boundaries.

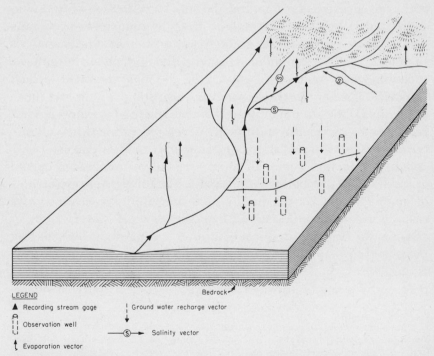

LEGEND

▲ Recording stream gage   ⵏ Ground water recharge vector

ᴀ
ᵢ ᵢ Observation well
ᴜ   ──⑤─► Salinity vector

ⵏ Evaporation vector

FIG. 2.1. Defining a water-resource system for simulation. The supply configuration for a sample basin.

To define the important supply relationships we must rely on the basic studies of climatology, hydrology, topography, geology, soils, and land use that are common to modern water-resource planning endeavors.[2] Information from these preliminary studies must be translated into analytical relationships for use in simulation. For example, evaporation from a reservoir can be approximated by a function of climate and surface area; this last can be mapped into a function of reservoir contents. Finally, to account for statistical variation in climate, the expression might include a stochastic component.

The simulation program for the Lehigh River system is concerned only with surface water. While there are significant supplies of ground water in the Lehigh basin, detailed data on their occurrence and relationship to surface flows are lacking; thus, ground water could not reliably be considered in the simulation program. Because reservoir sites are located in forested uplands, sedimentation is not a significant factor; evaporation from reservoirs can also be neglected as inconsequential in this relatively cool, humid region. The supply configuration of the Lehigh system thus can be adequately defined by the stream courses shown in Fig. 2.2. Detailed data on runoff are analyzed with respect to this stream configuration.

Water demands. Here we identify the points or zones, present or potential, which draw upon the water resources of the system.[3] Examples of points of water use are urban areas drawing domestic, commercial, and industrial water supplies, areas of potential irrigation development, stream reaches useful for navigation, zones or points of power demand, and areas suitable for management of recreation and fish and wildlife. Zones of substantial flood hazard or of deficient water quality must also be defined.

Recalling that detailed simulation is the terminal step in the

[2] See, for example, the natural-resource studies listed in:
    (a) *Delaware River basin*, reference 1.
    (b) *Potomac River basin report*, reference 1.
    (c) United Nations Economic Commission for Asia and the Far East, *Multiple-purpose river basin development*, pt. 1, *Manual of river basin planning* (1955).

[3] Points or zones of water use may lie outside the river basin being studied. It is unimportant whether an out-of-basin water use, such as New York City's use of water from the Delaware basin, is described as "outside the system" (if the system is defined in areal terms as the river basin) or "inside the system" (if the system is expanded areally insofar as this water use is concerned).

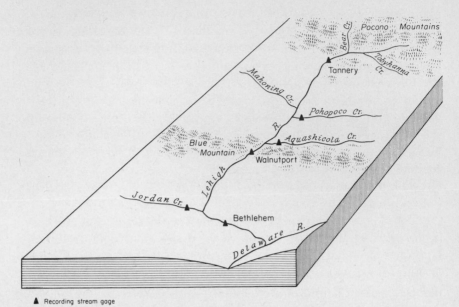

▲ Recording stream gage

FIG. 2.2 Defining a water-resource system for simulation. The supply configuration for the Lehigh basin example.

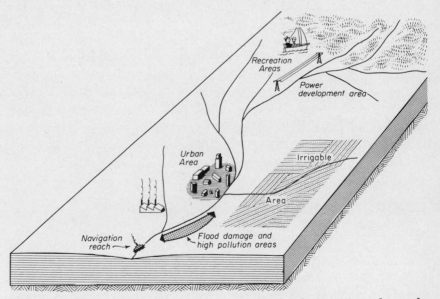

FIG. 2.3. Defining a water-resource system for simulation. Water demands and problems for a sample basin.

planning process, we rely on earlier analyses of population, urban and rural land use and economic activity to locate or identify major use points or problem areas.[4] Figure 2.3 illustrates how water uses and problems are defined for a sample basin, while Fig. 2.4 depicts the relevant water demands and problems for the Lehigh system. In our example, demands for water supply and problems of flood damage and water quality are concentrated in the lower reaches of the main stem, centering on the cities of Allentown and Bethlehem. In contrast, demands for electric energy and for water-based recreation services are regional in scope, extending far beyond the basin boundaries to include the Philadelphia and New York metropolitan areas.

Development measures. The concern is with identifying the most promising possibilities, including nonstructural and structural measures, for meeting the water demands and alleviating the water problems. Along with the dams, reservoirs, hydroelectric power plants, levees, channel improvements, and water transmission and diversion works, there are facilities for ground-water pumping, water spreading, waste-treatment, recreation, and a variety of

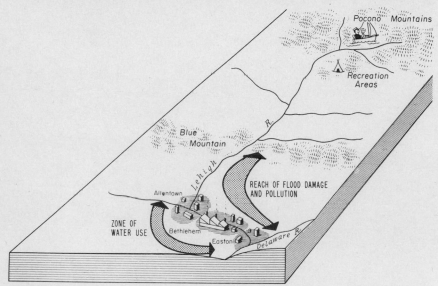

FIG. 2.4. Defining a water-resource system for simulation. Water demands and problems for the Lehigh basin example.

[4] See, for example, *Delaware River basin*, reference 1, vols. II, IX and *Potomac River basin report*, reference 1, vols. V–IX.

management and regulatory systems such as flood-plain zoning, flood warning, and water-quality control. Development possibilities may transcend basin boundaries; for example, a ground-water aquifer which intersects watershed limits may be developed and managed as a single hydrologic entity; and surface water may be diverted to adjacent river basins for irrigation, domestic or industrial use.

As pointed out above, the number of development alternatives would ordinarily be reduced prior to simulation analysis by preliminary screening techniques to those few showing the most promise. In most cases some form of preliminary screening is necessary because computer simulation increases rapidly in complexity and difficulty as the number of alternative development possibilities grows; a substantial reduction in the number of alternatives at an early stage is therefore desirable.

A set of development possibilities appropriate for the sample case shown on Figs. 2.1 and 2.3 is depicted on Fig. 2.5. Note that

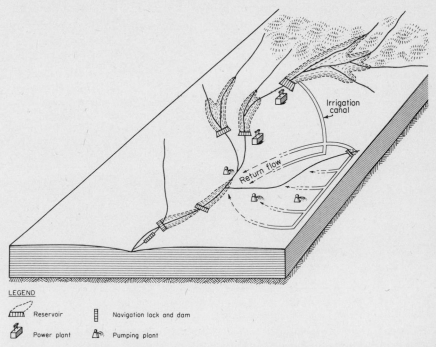

LEGEND

Reservoir   Navigation lock and dam

Power plant   Pumping plant

FIG. 2.5. Defining a water-resource system for simulation. Development measures for a sample basin.

multiple-purpose reservoirs, diversion dams, irrigation canals, water-supply aqueducts, power plants, channel improvements, water spreading works, and ground-water pumping plants are included, all as interrelated parts of a system designed to provide domestic and industrial water supply, irrigation, electric power, navigation, water quality management, and flood damage reduction. Thus, both small- and large-scale components might survive the preliminary screening step.

The Lehigh basin example is shown in Fig. 2.6. Following our preliminary screening of alternatives, there remain six storage sites, which are identified in the simulation program and the text by the numbers 1 through 6. Reservoirs 1 and 2 (Tobyhanna and Bear Creek) are alternatives; any system design can include one of these reservoirs but not both.[5] In effect, we deal with alternative system designs which can include up to five reservoirs.

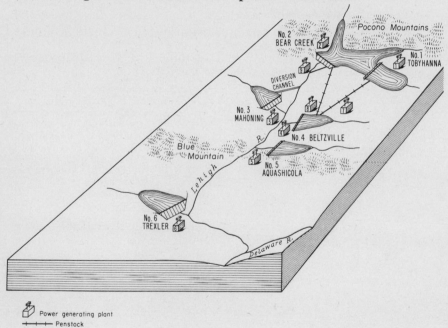

FIG. 2.6. Defining a water-resource system for simulation. Development measures for the Lehigh basin example.

[5] There is an existing reservoir at Bear Creek with 108×10^3 acre ft capacity used solely for flood control. References to Bear Creek throughout relate to its total capacity, existing plus planned, although capital and OMR costs are appended only to proposed increases in size.

Each reservoir can be used to provide (i) regulated flows for water supply or water quality improvement at Bethlehem, (ii) recreation services at the reservoir site, (iii) storage for flood-damage prevention, and (iv) hydroelectric energy.

As shown in Fig. 2.6., a diversion channel can be provided from the Lehigh River at a point below reservoirs 1 and 2 to reservoir 3 (Mahoning) so that flows in the Lehigh can be diverted and stored, if desired, in reservoir 3, which thereby functions as an off-channel storage unit.

Reservoirs 3, 4 (Beltzville), 5 (Aquashicola), and 6 (Trexler) are each associated with but a single hydroelectric power plant location. But, as shown in Fig. 2.6, reservoirs 1 and 2 can have more than one (although only one for each design). Actually, there are five variations, called *Cases*, which exist in conjunction with reservoirs 3–6. These Cases and the associated power turbine assignments are shown in Table 2.1.

Selection of a specific system design implies selection of only

TABLE 2.1. Cases for Lehigh system designs, with associated reservoir and turbine numbers and power plant locations.

Case	Reservoir no.	Turbine no.[a]	Location of power plant
1	1	1	At the dam site discharging into the Lehigh directly below the dam site. Called "no-pipe."
2	1	7	At end of a tunnel plus a high-head penstock, discharging into reservoir 4 (Beltzville). Called "Beltzville pipe."
3	2	2	At the dam site discharging into the Lehigh directly below the dam site. Called "no-pipe."
4	2	9	At the end of a high-head penstock, discharging into the Lehigh, several miles below the dam site. Called "Lehigh pipe."
5	2	8	At the end of a tunnel plus high-head penstock discharging into reservoir 4 (Beltzville). Called "Beltzville pipe."

[a] Turbines 3–6 are assigned to reservoirs 3–6, respectively, and are invariant for all cases.

one Case, because reservoirs 1 and 2 are alternatives and for each reservoir there can be only one power plant.[6]

Conjunctive use of ground water. Although our study of the Lehigh River system does not explicitly include the analysis of utilization of ground-water resources, their inclusion in a simulation study poses no major difficulties. An analysis of water-logging and salinity of agricultural lands in West Pakistan, in which a group of Harvard water-resource analysts participated, demonstrates that the greatest difficulty lies in proper formulation of the physical relationships rather than in the formalism of the simulation technique.[7] A four-season model is postulated for the Pakistan study. Inflows to the model are diversions from the Indus River system and rainfall; values of both the streamflow and rainfall are generated by means of operational hydrology models analogous to those utilized in the Lehigh River simulation and described in the next section.[8] The central feature of the irrigation scheme is a large well field, from which the effluent is recycled to join with the direct irrigation diversion and rainfall. Leakage occurs from the watercourses directly to an aquifer, the remaining water being applied to the land.

A portion of the applied water leaves the system through evapotranspiration, and the residual flows downward as throughput to the aquifer. Because of the hot and arid climate, evaporation losses occur directly from the ground-water surface; additional depletion occurs by seepage from the elevated ground water into canals and ditches. The problem is to devise optimal patterns for pumping, irrigation releases, well spacing, and crop selection.

The details of this study are not relevant here, but it is instructive to note certain similarities between simulating a ground-water

[6] The Lehigh system of developments includes the four reservoirs contained in the Corps of Engineers recommended plan for the Lehigh basin—Bear Creek (raised), Beltzville, Aquashicola, and Trexler—plus two reservoirs not recommended by the Corps—Mahoning and Tobyhanna—and power plants associated with all dams (also not recommended by the Corps). See *Delaware River basin*, reference 1, vol. I.

[7] *Report on land and water development in the Indus plain*, White House–Department of the Interior Panel on Waterlogging and Salinity in West Pakistan (Washington, D.C., January 1964), and H. A. Thomas, Jr. and R. Burden, *Indus river basin studies*, Final Report to the Science Adviser, Washington, D.C. (1965).

[8] We have adopted the term "operational hydrology" in this book for the process of generating synthetic traces of streamflow or rainfall. An alternative term suggested by others is "stochastic hydrology."

and a surface-water system. Continuity is essential to each model; just as reservoir inflows and outflows are added algebraically to produce a change in reservoir storage, so are ground-water sources and losses (for example, seepage, canal leakage, evaporation) combined to impute a variable ground-water level in each time-interval of the simulation. The operating policies which govern these systems differ vastly in their scope and complexity, but in the hands of a skillful analyst, the flexibility and diversity of the modern, high-speed digital computer are enormous so that the computer is applicable to both ground- and surface-water problems. Schemes for generating inputs, surface or subsurface, can be devised for either model.

ORGANIZING AND ANALYZING STREAMFLOW DATA

The simulation analysis described in this book is designed primarily to utilize long synthetic streamflow traces derived by statistical analysis of parameters of the historical record. In fact, much of the value of simulation analysis depends on the characterization of expected system performance over very long periods — say several hundred years — for only through analysis of such long records can a statistically adequate measure of system stability be obtained. Because historical records are available typically for periods of less than fifty years, synthetic traces are necessary for these long simulations.

The simulation program for the Lehigh system accepts as input either operational hydrology or the actual historical record. In either case the hydrologic data required by the program are of two forms: mean monthly flows and mean three-hourly flows. The three-hour increment is the largest that could be conveniently used considering the concentration time of the sub-basins and the flood travel times through channel reaches. These values are required at the six control points (reservoirs 1–6) and at two points (Walnutport and Bethlehem) where the effects of control are measured.

There follows (i) a description of the methods used to generate (a) monthly operational hydrology and (b) synthetic flood hydrographs with three-hourly readings; and (ii) a discussion of the conversion of data from the actual record into forms appropriate for use in the Lehigh system simulation. The monthly and flood flows are regenerated for each simulation run. Alternatively, these data can be produced initially and stored on tape for use in each subsequent run, but the computing speed of the IBM 7094 (the computer used to run the Lehigh simulation program) is so high that it is more efficient to regenerate the data. That is, the mechanical delay associated with reading tape exceeds the electronic delay required for computing the values.

The monthly operational hydrology generator. This section presents an outline of a mathematical model for generating monthly operational hydrology, but acceptance of simulation as a design technique does not imply acceptance of the particular model proposed here. Conversely, one might agree that the model is a reasonable representation of the governing stochastic process in a river basin, while specifically rejecting the use of simulation as an aid in the design process. In any event, a simulation program can be executed with a different operational hydrology generator by simply substituting a compatible subroutine; indeed, as stated above, operational hydrology can be bypassed completely in favor of the historical record.

Computation of synthetic monthly inflows is a trivial numerical matter; our justification for the simple linear relationships incorporated in the model includes substantial doses of statistical theory, inappropriate in this work, but the details of the analysis appear in the statistical literature,[9] and the interested reader may consult the appropriate derivations.

The use of a Markov model to generate flows is reported in the literature.[10] These early efforts are predicated on a normal distribution of the flow data, or on some transform, such as logarithmic, which renders the data normal. Thomas and Fiering [11] show that to treat non-normal distributions it is sufficient to alter the distribu-

[9] M. B. Fiering, "A multivariate model for synthesis of streamflows," *J. Hydraulics Div., Am. Soc. Civil Engrs. 90 HY 5*, 43 (September 1964).

[10] See H. A. Thomas, Jr., and M. B. Fiering, "The mathematical synthesis of streamflow sequences," chap. 12 of A. Maass, M. Hufschmidt, R. Dorfman, H. Thomas, S. Marglin and G. Fair, *Design of water-resource systems* (Harvard University Press, Cambridge, 1962); and M. B. Fiering, "Queueing theory and simulation in reservoir design," *Trans. Am. Soc. Civil Engrs., 127*, 1114 (1962).

[11] H. A. Thomas, Jr., and M. B. Fiering, *Operations research in water quality management*, report of the Harvard Water Resources Group to the U.S. Public Health Service (1963).

tion of the random additive component and thus maintain higher moments of the observed data. For example,

$$x_{i+1} = \mu + \beta(x_i - \mu) + t_{i+1}\sigma(1 - \rho^2)^{1/2} \tag{2.1}$$

represents a linear regression model between flows in successive time periods. In this model, x_{i+1}, the flow in the $(i+1)^{st}$ interval, is a linear function of x_i, the flow in the ith interval; of a standardized random deviate t_{i+1}; and of the population parameters μ, β, σ, and ρ. In accordance with standard statistical notation, μ is the population mean, σ the population standard deviation, β the regression coefficient of flows in the $(i+1)^{st}$ interval on values in the ith interval, and ρ the correlation coefficient between flows in successive time periods. The standardized deviate has zero mean and unit variance. If the x_i are normally distributed, t is also normally distributed whence the mean and variance of x_{i+1} are preserved. If the x_i are derived from a parent gamma-distribution, it is necessary and sufficient that the standardized random deviates t_{i+1} be distributed like gamma, with skewness dependent upon, but not equal to, the skewness of the observed x_i.

The model described in Eq. (2.1) is particularly simple to apply because the population parameters do not change with time. In the general case, exemplified by the Lehigh simulation, the year is divided into a repetitive cycle of seasons or months. Double subscripts in the following model take account of the seasonal variation:

$$x_{i,j} = \mu_j + \beta_j(x_{i-1,j-1} - \mu_{j-1}) + t_{i,j}\sigma_j(1 - \rho_j^2)^{1/2} \tag{2.2}$$

In this equation, j is the index on months and runs from 1 to 12; β_j and ρ_j are the regression and correlation coefficients, respectively, between seasons j and $j-1$. If N years of synthetic flow are desired, the index i runs from 1 to N. As in the simple model, Eq. (2.1), the distribution of the $t_{i,j}$ can be so altered that the resulting sequence of x-values is appropriately distributed. For a gamma-distribution, the skewness of the t-values (γ_t) depends upon the skewness coefficients which obtain in months j and $j-1$, whence the necessary adjustments vary with each month of the annual cycle. The formula is

$$\gamma_t = (\gamma_j - \rho_j^3\gamma_{j-1})/(1 - \rho_j^2)^{3/2}.$$

In earlier efforts to synthesize flows at several sites in a basin,[12] the model in Eq. (2.2) is called the "serial correlation" component of operational hydrology. From among all the stations under analysis it is necessary to identify a key station or stations — perhaps that station with the longest or most complete record or perhaps that station whose flows appear most strongly correlated with the other observations — at which the record is extended by means of serial correlation. From the extended record, "cross correlation" is utilized to estimate the flows at all the other sites. Cross correlation, like serial correlation, involves a linear regression model and a stochastic or random additive component; the only difference is that the variables are spatially rather than temporally related. Thus, to estimate $y_{i,j,k}$ (the flow at the kth satellite) from x (the flow at the key station or site whose record is already extended) in the jth month of the ith year we write

$$y_{i,j,k} = \mu_{j,k} + \beta_{j,k}(x_{i,j} - \nu_j) + t_{i,j,k}\sigma_{j,k}(1 - \rho_{j,k}^2)^{1/2} \qquad (2.3)$$

The term $\mu_{j,k}$ is the mean of the kth dependent variate, and ν_j is the mean of the independent or key variate in month j. The parameters of the regression equations carry two subscripts to identify the relevant month and site. In practice, several satellite or y-stations are estimated from a single key station, so that the subscript k identifies the dependent variable.

It can be demonstrated that the univariate marginal distributions at each site are maintained by this model, but it is manifest that the model ignores the serial correlation coefficient at each satellite station; thus the technique fails to preserve a relevant characteristic of the original hydrologic data. Furthermore, in a large basin, where the input data are interdependent and intertwined, no clear strategy exists for identifying that single, most important, site to serve as the key station, or trunk, from which all the other branches emanate.

Our proposed hydrology model substitutes for the key-station approach a mathematical algorithm which preserves the relevant moments at each satellite station and maintains the several serial correlations as well.[13]

Let the original input variates $x_{i,j,k}$ be subject to a principal

[12] Maass, Hufschmidt, *et al*, reference 10, chap. 12.

[13] The key station approach was actually used in setting up the Lehigh simulation, but the new algorithm described below was used in the simulation program for the Delaware system, described in Chapter 5.

component analysis,[14] one analysis for each of the 12 arrays of monthly data. The output of this computation is a set of coefficients which transforms the original input variables into a set of linearly independent (orthogonal) components. For example, let there be n sites in the basin, so that n orthogonal components are constructed from the n observations in a particular month. If the index k runs from 1 to n, we may write, for the ith month in the jth year,

$$z_{i,j,k} = a_{1,j,k}x_{i,j,1} + a_{2,j,k}x_{i,j,2} + \ldots + a_{n,j,k}x_{i,j,n} \qquad (2.4)$$

Here $z_{i,j,k}$, the $(i,j)^{\text{th}}$ value of the kth principal component, is a linear combination of the n observations made during the $(i,j)^{\text{th}}$ interval. A cubic array $(12 \times n \times n)$ of coefficients $a_{i,j,k}$ is required to specify all n principal components; each plane of this array of coefficients comprises the eigenvectors of the correlation matrix and is computed directly from the matrix of (monthly) bivariate correlation coefficients which obtain between each pair of stations.

The principal components have the property of linear independence, and in a sense they represent artificial stations, each of which is treated like a real station, with the important simplification that each such artificial station is numerically and causally unrelated to any other. This means that the principal components at each of the fictitious sites can be extended using serial correlation alone, and no account need be taken of cross-correlation because, by definition, each fictitious site is independent of all others. This makes the computation particularly simple, it being necessary only to evaluate the principal components from the historical record and to compute the handful of serial correlation coefficients which obtain at the fictitious sites. All principal components can be extended indefinitely, whereupon their numerical values in any time interval can be recombined by an inverse linear transform to reconstitute or synthesize flows at the given sites. The inverse transform preserves all the moments of the original data, the several serial correlations, and all of the cross correlations. In other words, the synthetic data are samples from the same parent distributions as the original hydrologic observations; the synthetic flows are thereby statistically indistinguishable from the observed flows.

The historical record of monthly flows is subject to extensive analysis prior to operation of the simulation program. First, the

[14] M. G. Kendall, A course in multivariate analysis (Hafner, New York, 1957).

record must be analyzed for extraction of principal components. Second, the principal components are subject to serial correlation analysis. Third, the inverse transform must be computed so that the extended data at the fictitious sites can be recombined to produce flows at the original gaging stations, or, more generally, at the associated dam sites.

Given the derived coefficients, the operation of our synthetic hydrology model is extremely simple. During each month of the simulation, the program computes the current values of all n components, using a model similar to Eq. (2.2). The only difference is that the x's are replaced by z's and the parameters, instead of defining the distribution of the x's, pertain to the distributions of the z's. Finally, using an inverse transform,

$$x_{i,j,k} = b_{1,j,k} z_{i,j,1} + b_{2,j,k} z_{i,j,2} + \ldots + b_{n,j,k} z_{i,j,n} \qquad (2.5)$$

the z-values are recombined to produce synthetic flow values at the original gaging sites. It might be necessary to adjust the resulting x-values so that the flows are reckoned at the dam sites; alternatively, the adjustment could be made among the original input variates so that the derived coefficients pertain to the dam sites rather than the gaging stations. This is a matter of choice; we make the adjustments to the original input variables. Coding the generating algorithm poses no difficulty since the FORTRAN language (the pseudo-language used for coding the Lehigh and Delaware simulation programs) is particularly flexible and efficient with respect to indexing linear systems. Details of the logic are given in subsequent sections.

It should be emphasized that our simulation analysis admits two, and only two, types of hydrologic data, that is, historical and synthetic. Creation of missing flow data, based on linear or multiple regression, proportional evaluation, or regional analyses, for the purpose of constructing a complete historic record, is not always a useful approach for simulation analysis. Depending upon the objective, the correlation, and the length of missing and observed records, it is possible to evaluate the utility of filling in the gaps, and Fiering [15] gives a tabular solution to this problem as part of a more general investigation.

[15] M. B. Fiering, "On the use of correlation to augment data," *J. Am. Stat. Assoc.,* 57, 20 (1962).

The flood generator. In contrast to the simplicity with which our monthly operational hydrology generator can be exchanged with other generating models, the synthesis of flood flows is intimately interwoven with the fabric of the Lehigh simulation program, and is divided into two distinct phases. The first, or generating, phase is a sequence of computations for constructing flood hydrographs at 8 sites (reservoir sites 1–6, Walnutport, and Bethlehem); this sequence could be replaced by schemes more suitable for other hydrologic regimes. The second, or routing, phase is closely intertwined with the logic of the operating policy. Data manipulations for generating the floods and the strategy for making and routing flood releases are discussed below.

The program performs a linear regression of daily peak flow on monthly discharge in order to estimate the daily peak corresponding to a (synthetically generated) monthly discharge.[16] Under input option the program can perform the regressions using a logarithmic transform of the dependent and independent variables. Examination of the Lehigh data and of several test runs indicates such a transform is desirable, and all subsequent references to the flood-estimating procedure imply a prior logarithmic transform. By means of a multiplicative factor the daily peak flow is converted (that is, increased) to a value corresponding to the 3-hour peak.[17] A time-of-peak for Bethlehem is chosen at random from the spectrum of integers between 1 and 240, where the units are 3-hour time-intervals; times of peak at the remaining 7 sites are computed by subtracting the lag (an input variable) at each site from the Bethlehem value.

Figure 2.7 indicates the geometric relationships developed in a typical flood. A flood event is defined by a 4-segment linear function, whence 5 points in the plane of volume and time are needed. These are numbered (1) through (5) on Fig. 2.7. Points (1) and (5) are anchored at zero ordinate and at abscissae corresponding to the beginning and end of the month, or 1 and 240 respectively. The duration is estimated as a linear function of the peak and volume, with

---

[16] The significance of the correlation, not merely the form of the relation, would have to be assured for each application. Certain hydrologic regimes (e.g., the long flat hydrographs on the Missouri River) are particularly adaptable; others are not.

[17] Daily peak flows were chosen for the linear regression analysis with monthly flows because, unlike 3-hour peak flows, the data were readily available from the streamflow records published by the U. S. Geological Survey.

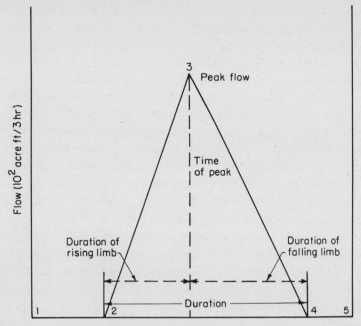

FIG. 2.7. Parameters for synthesis of flood hydrographs. Simple model adopted for Lehigh simulation program.

apportionment between rising and falling limbs selected at random but constrained to lie in a given range. For example, the fractions of the duration devoted to rising limbs in month i and at site j are presumed to be rectangularly distributed between two limits $u_{i,j}$ and $u'_{i,j}$, where $u_{i,j} \le u'_{i,j} \le 1$; the $u_{i,j}$ and $u'_{i,j}$ are input parameters. If the volume under the triangular wedge exceeds the monthly discharge, the duration is shortened until the volumes are brought into agreement or until the duration is reduced to 6 time units (18 hours), whereupon the program accepts the inconsistency and continues. If the monthly discharge exceeds the flood volume, no adjustment is made; that is, since base flow is set to zero in this model, and since the flood recession curve is neglected, the excess of monthly flow is presumed to be exactly accommodated by the ignored sectors of the hydrograph.

A series of boundary checks are made to insure that points (2) and (4) lie in the range 1 to 240; any failure to respect these constraints is adjusted to the left or right as required.

Our initial attempt to devise a flood-generating model represents a far more enterprising scheme than the method adopted. As shown in Fig. 2.8, points (2) and (4) lie on the sides of the triangular flood wedge, and the base flow for each site and month is read as a subscripted input datum. Moreover, the shape is frequently adjusted until the final volume under the hydrograph agrees exactly with the monthly discharge. However, efforts to bring the flood and monthly volumes into balance introduce some distortions which ultimately undermine the entire scheme because the generated peak flows are often significantly changed. The peaks arise from reliable estimates; that is, in the Lehigh system the correlations between peaks and means are very high, say of the order of 0.90 to 0.95, and any fitting technique which alters such highly stable relationships in the name of maintaining volumetric consistency is clearly inappropriate. Under certain hydrological regimes, this more detailed model could be adapted for use and inserted in the program, but this is not feasible for the Lehigh system.

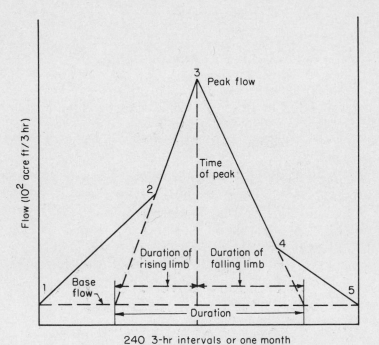

FIG. 2.8. Parameters for synthesis of flood hydrographs. First version of model devised for use in the Lehigh simulation program.

Total similitude is sacrificed in this, as in every, model. There is no way, short of reconstituting the prototype, to assure identity. But the relevant question in any model study must be, "Does this model adequately approach reality?" Of course, what is adequate in one context may be inadequate in another; thus our flood model could not serve to describe all of the underlying hydrologic components at work in a flood. But, as a guide to decision-making in this simulation study, the failure of our model to reproduce nature exactly is not considered detrimental. Thus, the sensitivity of response, not necessarily the machine capability, should limit the complexity of model formulations.

We generate peaks at the 6 reservoirs, at Walnutport, and at Bethlehem. Two intermediate stations are created, corresponding to the unregulated flows above Walnutport and between Walnutport and Bethlehem. The peaks at these stations are estimated by subtraction; thus the unregulated peak flow above Walnutport, P'_W, is given by

$$P'_W = P_W - P_1 - P_2 - P_3 - P_4 - P_5,$$

and the unregulated peak flow between Walnutport and Bethlehem, P'_B, is estimated by

$$P'_B = P_B - P_W - P_6,$$

where P_i is the peak flow at station i, and P_B, P_W are the generated peaks at Bethlehem and Walnutport, respectively. Because reservoirs 1 and 2 are alternatives, when $P_1 \neq 0$, $P_2 = 0$; and, conversely, when $P_2 \neq 0$, $P_1 = 0$.

Subsequent computations are based on flows at the 6 reservoir sites and the 2 intermediate flows; the floods at Walnutport and Bethlehem are synthesized anew by routing the constituent flows to these two sites.[18]

Linear interpolation between pairs of adjacent points gives a complete hydrograph; this computation is performed at reservoirs 1–6 and for the intermediate or unregulated flows above Walnutport and between Walnutport and Bethlehem. The flows above

[18] This approach of synthesizing floods at Walnutport and Bethlehem by routing the upstream flows was adopted at the suggestion of Corps of Engineers specialists in flood hydrology. While some gain was obtained in consistency among flows at the eight points, the resultant peak flows at Walnutport and Bethlehem were significantly lower than peaks as originally generated by the model.

Walnutport are routed to Walnutport, using the modified Gilchrist technique [19] and are there added to the unregulated inflow. The total synthesized Walnutport flow is routed to Bethlehem and added to the flow from reservoir 6 and the unregulated flow above Bethlehem; this gives a total Bethlehem flow. If either the Walnutport or Bethlehem peak exceeds the appropriate channel capacity, a flood is presumed to exist and the special routing routine is called.

The routing routine supervises releases on a 3-hourly basis during periods of high flows. Its operation is to apportion releases among the reservoirs 1, 2, 3, 4, and·5 so that the probability of spill in the next 3-hour period is equal for all reservoirs, this being accomplished by means of a rule described in Chapter 3. Releases up to the channel capacities are tolerated, whereupon the gates are closed and the reservoirs begin to encroach upon the flood-storage capacity. Of course, any inevitable spills are routed downstream, and damage estimates are made using the appropriate polynomial function.

As in the case of the monthly hydrology, the program can bypass the synthetic flood-flow generator in order to use as input the historical flood data available on magnetic tape. The sensitivity analysis suggested earlier, whereby the effects of triangular representation of flood hydrographs can be evaluated, might be initiated using these actual flood data and their simplified, modeled representations.

Adjusting hydrologic data. In general, it is necessary to make a number of conversions and adjustments of hydrologic data to adapt the observations for use in simulation analysis. The adjustments made for the Lehigh simulation program, which are described in the paragraphs to follow, are typical.

For *monthly flows* it is necessary to convert from units of cubic feet per second for a month, to hundreds of acre feet, to render the units of storage, monthly inflow, and monthly draft compatible and additive. We divide the year into 12 "standard" months of equal length (30.44 days) in order to simplify the simulation; consequently it is necessary to effect small changes in the observed monthly volumes, adding a little here and subtracting a little there, to assure continuity within a repetitive annual cycle. These two

[19] For a description of this technique, see *Delaware River basin*, reference 1, vol. VI, p. M–65.

adjustments (conversion to hundreds of acre feet and allowance for standard months) as well as all conversions and adjustments discussed in subsequent sections, are coded for the IBM 7094 computer. The expenditure of effort and money in this unsophisticated use of the computer is justified because it avoids the high degree of unreliability traditionally associated with manual card-punching. Thus, after proofreading the initial file of punched data cards, it is unnecessary to intervene with further manual key-punching because the programs provide output directly on cards in BCD (Binary Coded Decimal) mode and in a format suitable for re-use as input.

For those cases where the gaging site does not correspond to the dam site or use point, it is necessary to make a further adjustment based on drainage area ratios. For the Lehigh, data at 5 gaging stations are key-punched into cards, from which flows at the 6 dam sites, at Tannery, and at Bethlehem are computed as shown in Table 2.2.

Table 2.2. Drainage area relationships between gaging stations and dam sites, Lehigh River system.

Gaging station	Drainage area (sq. mi.)	Relevant dam site or use point	Drainage area (sq. mi.)	Ratio of drainage area at dam site to drainage area at gaging station
Tannery	322	Tobyhanna	224	0.695
		Bear Creek	288	0.895
Pohopoco Creek	109	Mahoning	39	0.358
		Beltzville	75	0.690
Aquashicola Creek	77	Aquashicola	66	0.865
Jordan Creek	76	Trexler	51	0.675
Bethlehem	1279	Bethlehem	1279	1.000

Each record is then examined for gaps. Principal component analysis of the hydrologic record requires hydrologic data in an intact rectangular array with dimensions equal to the number of sites and the number of observations. From this array, the correlation coefficient matrix is computed, whereupon the eigenvalues and eigenvectors are extracted. If a few data are missing from the array, they should be estimated by a suitable correlation or regression technique. Of course, it is possible to compute the bivariate correlation coefficients between the record at any two sites regardless of the temporal configuration of the other observations. It can be shown that the eigenvalues and eigenvectors are meaningful even if all elements of the correlation coefficient matrix do not pertain to the same time span. In either case, whether the elements of the correlation coefficient matrix are obtained from an analysis of a neat rectangular array or, more typically, from a data array characterized by incomplete records, the principal components are evaluated; the relevant coefficients are automatically punched directly from magnetic output tape onto cards. These coefficients are the parameters of the serial correlation model and the inverse transformation model described above.

For the Lehigh, the basic correlation matrix is predicated on streamflow records covering the periods of observation shown in Table 2.3. A complete streamflow record for these stations was

TABLE 2.3 Periods of streamflow records used in hydrologic analyses of the Lehigh River system

Gaging station	Period of record used
Bethlehem	October 1922–September 1960
Tannery	October 1922–September 1960
Walnutport	October 1946–September 1960
Pohopoco Creek	October 1940–September 1960
Aquashicola Creek	October 1939–September 1960
Jordan Creek	October 1944–September 1960

constructed for the period October 1922–September 1960 by filling in the missing data at some stations for early years with a simple bivariate regression on either Bethlehem or Tannery. Examination of the correlations involved indicates a gain in information for the sites which comprise the Lehigh system when the records are augmented. Thus the extended historical record serves two purposes: (1) it provides the data from which the parameters of the operational hydrology generator are estimated (that is, by defining estimates of the population moments of the streamflows) and (2) it serves as input for simulation under historical conditions.

The means and standard deviations of monthly flows for the six stations, as derived from the augmented record, are shown in Table 2.4.

Three-hourly flood flows. Adjustments in 3-hourly flows are similar to those for monthly flows, although there are some important differences. While the unit conversion from cfs to acre ft remains the same, the areal adjustment differs because a linear relation does not serve to transform an observed peak flow from the gaging station to the dam site. We assume, following Linsley [20] *et al.*, that logarithms of peak flows are related to each other in proportion to the logarithms of their respective drainage areas, so the requisite conversions are nonlinear. Because the regressions of peaks on monthly flows (used in the flood-flow generator) pertain, respectively, to mean daily peaks and mean monthly flows, it is necessary to convert generated daily peaks to 3-hourly peaks. This is done by deriving a set of average ratios (of 3-hour peak to daily peak for all stations and all months) from the observed flood hydrographs.

The construction of a complete set of 240 3-hourly readings to introduce the historical floods requires much interpolation of data because detailed hydrographs are available for only a small fraction of the month—that portion of the month subject to flooding—and even these hydrographs are not available for all stations and for all floods of record. Standard hydrologic techniques are therefore applied to convert the scanty historical data on flood flows to estimates of historical flood data for the entire month at each site.

It must be emphasized that each completed task described in this section is the final result of a painstaking process. Key-punching, incessant proofreading, attention to the minutiae of decimal points and rounding, and other thankless aspects of data collection and editing underlie all the subsequent analysis. It need hardly be mentioned that a complete and extensive filing system must be maintained for the punched data. A card color code, sliding metal drawers, and any other bookkeeping device which increases order and decreases risk of misplacing even a single card is desirable. As subsequent simulation studies are undertaken, it is reasonable to expect that data collection and preparation will proceed far more smoothly, particularly since the increased use of continuous re-

[20] R. K. Linsley, M. Kohler, and J. Paulhus, *Applied hydrology* (McGraw Hill, New York, 1949), pp. 572ff.

TABLE 2.4. Means and standard deviations (10³ acre ft) of monthly streamflows, Lehigh River basin, from historical record

Month	Bethlehem	Tannery	Walnutport	Pohopoco Creek	Aquashicola Creek	Jordan Creek
			Means			
January	146.54	40.28	131.47	13.22	9.77	9.04
February	153.92	39.28	131.57	13.41	10.11	10.05
March	237.13	66.00	181.65	19.06	15.67	12.91
April	227.34	74.18	211.11	18.88	14.46	10.34
May	165.76	52.62	156.64	16.97	11.58	8.16
June	111.48	31.23	78.93	10.32	6.75	4.34
July	105.33	27.47	77.78	10.34	8.15	4.75
August	85.92	21.28	67.48	7.53	6.35	4.56
September	72.31	19.21	43.23	5.90	5.61	3.49
October	85.43	26.38	58.06	6.64	5.52	3.46
November	128.48	41.03	112.88	10.43	9.42	6.56
December	148.64	43.79	147.98	13.67	10.73	8.93
			Standard Deviations			
January	77.18	21.02	67.72	6.70	5.57	6.07
February	71.23	19.80	50.41	5.73	3.97	4.72
March	102.95	28.89	43.56	5.32	4.57	4.35
April	80.21	29.15	63.94	7.41	5.92	5.16
May	71.69	23.55	68.18	7.98	5.58	4.77
June	49.20	14.93	32.00	4.89	2.99	2.77
July	81.92	25.78	71.14	10.31	8.48	4.06
August	72.64	26.14	81.97	16.23	7.10	7.08
September	62.79	16.95	32.87	5.70	4.86	3.50
October	66.45	24.40	72.93	7.12	4.96	4.69
November	84.58	26.68	60.13	5.86	6.29	4.33
December	89.42	26.74	82.85	8.52	6.23	4.80

corders, electronic processing equipment, and cards or tape for data storage will reduce the card-punching task with which we were faced.

SYSTEM DESIGN VARIABLES, PARAMETERS, AND CONSTANTS

With the general configuration of the system defined, the set of alternative water use and control measures specified, and the hydrologic data organized in useful form, the next task is to establish the physical limits of system components — say, the range of storage capacity at a reservoir site, or the range of aqueduct capacity — and to define the physical parameters and constants that characterize internal system relationships.

In general, there are two classes of system components, parameters, and constants: (1) *design variables*, which we are free to change from one simulation run to the next, and (2) *invariant* physical functions, parameters, and constants of the water-resource system under study.

Design variables. The relevant design variables are identified when the system is defined as described above. The most promising reservoir sites, diversion and transmission works, and groundwater recharge areas emerge, and the purposes to be served are identified and use points specified. But there remains the task of setting the range over which each design variable will be allowed to change; after all, there is some practical upper limit to the size of a specific storage reservoir, while the lower limit is imposed by a reservoir of zero capacity.

In general, design variables are of three types:

(i) *physical facilities* — sizes of storage reservoirs, hydro power plants, irrigation canals, water supply aqueducts, pumping plants, water-spreading works, water and sewage treatment plants, levees, navigation works, and recreation facilities at reservoirs;

(ii) *system outputs* — demands or targets (with associated distribution within the year) for electric energy, irrigation water, industrial and domestic water supply, levels of water quality, and recreational opportunities; and

(iii) *operating-policy parameters* — allocations of reservoir space for dead storage (to collect sediment or to provide minimum power head), flood control storage, and storage for recreational purposes; and rules for storing, releasing and routing water through the system, including conjunctive operation of surface and ground water reservoirs.

Some design variables, such as large-scale physical facilities involving substantial capital and operating costs, or important system outputs yielding large benefits, are major elements in a system design. Others are of minor importance. But the distinguishing feature of a set of design variables is that each set specifies a particular water-resource system whose performance, and resulting costs and benefits, can be examined by means of simulation.

Invariant physical functions, parameters, and constants. This class of system components reflects physical relationships among elements in the system. Important examples are functions relating (i) head and reservoir pool area to reservoir storage, and (ii) reservoir evaporation loss to reservoir area. Others are (iii) the conversion factors and turbine and generator efficiency factors that translate units of water flow and head into units of electric energy; (iv) flood-routing parameters and constants, which account for travel time of flood waves and the natural storage capacity of stream reaches; and (v) parameters that define the rate of return flow from irrigated areas.[21] Once determined for the system, they usually remain fixed for all simulation runs. It is convenient, however, to treat them as inputs to the simulation program so they can be changed readily rather than defined as integrated parts of the program structure.

As an aid to understanding the role of design variables, parameters, and constants in simulation analysis, there follows a detailed description of these elements in the Lehigh System. This discussion will be most useful if it is read in conjunction with the detailed description of the Lehigh simulation program contained in Chapter 3.

The Lehigh System: major design variables. The simulation model of the Lehigh System is prescribed by the 42 major design variables listed in Table 2.5. Sixteen variables deal with structural components — sizes of the six reservoirs, nine power plants, and

---

[21] For examples of such functions, see Maass, Hufschmidt, *et al.*, reference 10, chaps. 7 and 9; and D. S. Lewis and L. A. Shoemaker, "Hydro system power analysis by digital computer," *Trans. Am. Soc. Civil Engrs.*, *128-1*, 1086 (1963).

TABLE 2.5. Major physical design variables, Lehigh system.

Variable	Reservoir or power plant number	Assumed range of capacity or output level	Unit of measurement
Components of system			
Reservoir	1	0–400	10^3 acre ft
	2	0–530	
	3	0–400	
	4	0–200	
	5	0–165	
	6	0–135	
Power plant	1	0– 50	10^3 kw[a]
	2	0–125	
	3	0–100	
	4	0– 75	
	5	0– 15	
	6	0– 10	
	7	0–260	
	8	0–350	
	9	0–175	
Diversion works: Lehigh River to reservoir	3	12–44	10^3 acre ft/mo
Allocations of reservoir capacity			
Dead storage: Reservoir	1	0–400	10^3 acre ft
	2	0–530	
	3	0–400	
	4	0–200	
	5	0–165	
	6	0–135	
Flood storage: Reservoir	1	0–150	10^3 acre ft
	2	0–200	
	3	0– 35	
	4	0– 75	
	5	0– 60	
	6	0– 40	
Target recreation level: Reservoir	1	103–202	ft
	2	210–318	
	3	83–196	
	4	90–193	
	5	58–158	
	6	83–142	

Table 2.5 (continued)

Variable	Reservoir or power plant number	Assumed range of capacity or out-put level	Unit of measurement
Recreation level, adjusted: [b]			
Reservoir	1	103–202	ft
	2	210–318	
	3	83–196	
	4	90–193	
	5	58–158	
	6	83–142	
Target output for water supply		23– 50	10^3 acre ft/mo
Target output for energy		0– 60	10^6 kwh/mo

[a] Installed capacity.
[b] The ranges of the adjusted recreation levels above bottom of pool for reservoirs 1–6 are set at the same values as the corresponding target recreation levels, in order to obtain the greatest possible flexibility in this aspect of the operating procedure.

the diversion works from the Lehigh River to reservoir 3. (See Fig. 2.6 for location of proposed structures.) At most, only five reservoirs and five power plants can be included in any one design. The capacity of the diversion works from the Lehigh River to reservoir 3 is considered to be a direct function of the capacity of reservoir 3, rather than an independent design variable. The functional relationship is shown in Fig. 2.9.

The ranges of the 16 variables include all facility sizes likely to be attractive economically. For reservoirs, the upper limit of the range is reached where expected energy output (which is itself a function of the hydrology and power head) obtainable from an increment of installed capacity begins to drop sharply. In fact, the upper limit of power plant size is computed by using the head and sustained yield associated with the highest assumed level of relevant reservoir storage capacity, and by assuming a 10 percent minimum annual capacity factor for power plant operation. This assumption requires that sufficient power plant capacity be available to use the assured *annual* water yield for power production over

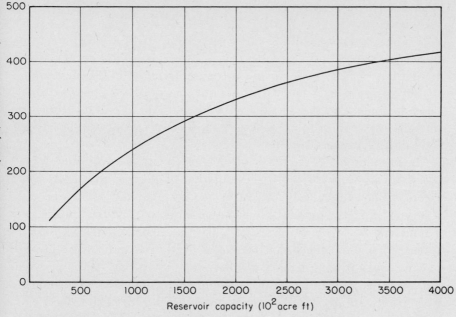

FIG. 2.9. Capacity of diversion tunnel from Lehigh River to reservoir 3 as a function of capacity of reservoir 3.

only one tenth of the year (or 10 times the prime power associated with the energy in the stream at given heads).

Twenty-four of the design variables relate to allocations of reservoir capacity; in a sense, they are parameters of the operating procedure. Of these, dead-storage capacity, once established for a design, is fixed for the life of the structure because it is an essential factor in the design and placement of the power plant or outlet works.

In contrast, flood-storage capacity need not be fixed. In fact, the allocation is allowed to vary month by month, in effect providing a 12-element vector of flood-storage allocation for each reservoir. Similarly, target recreation levels for reservoirs are vectors, with a separate element for each month. This allows high recreation levels to be maintained during the (summer) months of peak recreation demand without penalizing operation of the system during the off-season. Two such recreation level vectors are provided for each reservoir so that, if demands for other purposes cannot be met in any month without drawing the reservoir below the first, or upper, recreation level, a second level (equal to or lower than the first) is invoked.[22]

Although the flood-storage and recreation level allocations are allowed to assume different monthly values, we are not free to vary them from year to year during the simulation. The location and design of recreation facilities and the elevation of flood-control gates are based, in part, on the allocations to flood-control storage and the recreation pool storage. Ordinarily these vectors are fixed during any one simulation run.[23]

Thus the ranges of the reservoir design variables are deliberately broad to allow wide latitude in choice of design alternatives.[24] Dead-storage allocation is allowed to vary over the full range of reservoir capacity, and, in the extreme case, with maximum dead storage the reservoir would have a fixed recreation pool, no flood-storage allocation, no storage for withdrawal uses, and a fixed-head power plant utilizing reservoir inflows as they occur. The range of flood-storage allocations is set to provide complete control of floods with peaks approximately 100 percent greater than the flood of record.[25] Floods of such magnitude have a very low probability of occurrence. Recreation levels have an upper limit equal to the total storage capacity of the relevant reservoir; the lower limit for recreation is set at levels corresponding to zero capacity.

There remain two major variables—target outputs for water supply and for energy. The water supply target is interpreted to be a mean flow in the Lehigh River at Bethlehem; the energy target is specified as a total quantity of energy, available at the several power plants, for the entire system at a specified plant capacity factor.

[22] The rationale for providing two recreation levels instead of only one is the gain in flexibility in operating procedure which results. Further explanation is provided in Chapter 3.

[23] Water-resource planners will recognize the close similarity of these vectors to the conventional "rule curves" used in operating systems of reservoirs. In effect, each design specifies a set of such rule curves.

[24] It is recognized that when simulation analysis is used in the final stages of system design, the range of system design variables may have been reduced substantially by prior analyses to a relatively narrow band. In general, however, it is well to span a broad range of design variables in order to preserve flexibility in the design process, especially when such breadth can be preserved at little cost.

[25] These peaks are considerably in excess of those computed by the Corps of Engineers for the "standard project flood" which is defined as "the upper limit of hazard development against which protection would be sought." See *Delaware River basin*, reference 1, vol. VI, p. M–82.

The targets are expressed in annual quantities of water supply and energy and are characterized by monthly distributions. In effect, there are vectors for water-supply and energy targets, with separate values for each month. Typical monthly values, expressed as percentages of annual target outputs, are shown in Table 2.6.

The assumed range of annual target output for water supply is from 270,000 acre ft per year, the approximate minimum historical flow rate at Bethlehem with no regulation, to 570,000 acre ft per year, the Corps of Engineers estimate of projected water flow requirements at Bethlehem in 2010.[26]

The assumed range of annual target outputs for energy is from zero to 720,000,000 kilowatt-hours per year. This upper limit was set without regard to projected demands for energy in the market area; these demands far exceed the potential energy from streams in the Lehigh River basin. Rather, the upper limit is a liberal approximation of the maximum energy potential of the streams, taking into account power head and streamflow at all power sites considered in the design problem.

The Lehigh system: subsidiary design variables. Associated with the major design variables are a number of other input variables that either (a) are of minor significance in system design and operation, or (b) have values that are functions of the major variables.

TABLE 2.6. Monthly percentages of annual target outputs for water supply and energy.

Month	Water supply	Energy for plant factor (percent) of—			
		less than 20	20–39	40–60	100
January	7.7	12	11	10	8.33
February	7.7	12	10	9	8.33
March	8.3	12	9	8	8.33
April	8.3	1	6	7	8.33
May	8.3	1	4	7	8.33
June	9.0	2	6	7	8.33
July	9.0	10	7	7	8.33
August	9.0	10	8	8	8.33
September	8.4	10	9	9	8.33
October	8.3	10	9	9	8.33
November	8.3	10	10	9	8.33
December	7.7	10	11	10	8.33

[26] *Delaware River basin*, reference 1, vol. IX, p. Q–28, and Table Q–7, p. Q–30.

These subsidiary variables (other than those relative to power generation, which are discussed separately), three in number, are discussed below.

For each reservoir there is a vector of minimal channel flows below the reservoir for months 1–12. These serve as constraints on reservoir operation, that is, reservoir releases must maintain these flows no matter what the state of the system. Values of these minimal flows can be varied from one simulation run to the next, to give greater or lesser weight to aesthetic aspects and to maintenance of fish life.

Another set of design variables relates to estimates of expected cumulative inflows to reservoirs 3–6 for the period from the end of the current month to the end of the assumed reservoir refill period. For each reservoir there is a vector of such inflows for months 1–12; these are used in our reservoir release allocation rule [27] (applied in this model only to reservoirs 3–6) which equates (a) the proportions of each reservoir's space to total system reservoir space available after releases to (b) the proportions of each reservoir's estimated future inflow to total estimated reservoir inflow for the system. These estimates of future inflows can be based on mean monthly flows taken from the historical record, on flows with a selected frequency of occurrence, or on values computed from an inflow prediction model. In the Lehigh System we use mean monthly flows obtained from the record as the basis for these variables.

The upper limit of the damage-free flood flow at Bethlehem is a design variable that depends on the relationship of stage to discharge at Bethlehem (which may be modified by levees, channel improvements, and addition or clearance of encroachments on the flood plain) and upon economic development of the flood plain. This value may be varied to some extent under different assumptions of use and control of the flood plain.[28]

The Lehigh system: variables, functions, and constants relating to power generation. The several subsidiary variables associated with hydroelectric power include the penstock capacity and the

---

[27] Described in detail in Chapter 3, under *Monthly Operating Algorithm.*

[28] See G. F. White, *Choice of adjustment to floods,* University of Chicago, Dept. of Geography Research Paper No. 93 (Chicago, 1964), and R. W. Kates, *Industrial flood losses: damage estimation in the Lehigh valley,* University of Chicago, Dept. of Geography Research Paper No. 98 (Chicago, 1965).

so-called fixed factors of head for power plants 7, 8, or 9; the maximum heads for all power plants; and the turbine and generator efficiencies. Maximum heads at power plants 1–6 are straightforward functions of the total capacities, dead storages and maximum flood-storage allowances of reservoirs 1–6—all major design variables. These values may be obtained by reference to the head-capacity functions for the six reservoirs, as shown in Fig. 2.10. The fixed heads for turbines 7 and 8, which are also the maximum heads for those plants, are provided by the penstock drop as shown in Fig. 2.11. Five percent of this 872-ft drop is subtracted for friction losses to obtain the net effective head. Maximum head for power plant 9 is the sum of a fixed power head associated with the penstock plus a variable component which is a function of total storage capacity and maximum flood storage allowance in reservoir 2. Figure 2.12 depicts these relationships. The water capacities of the penstocks associated with turbines 7, 8, and 9 are functions of the power capacities of plants 7, 8, and 9.

A single factor is used to represent turbine and generator efficiences for all power plants. This factor appears as an input vari-

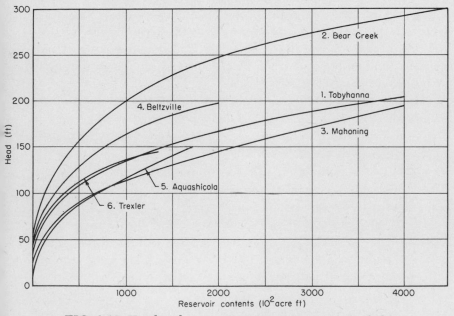

FIG. 2.10. Head and reservoir contents at reservoirs 1–6.

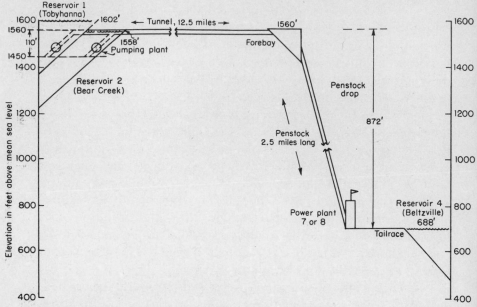

FIG. 2.11. Schematic diagram of reservoirs 1, 2, and 4, and Beltzville pipe.

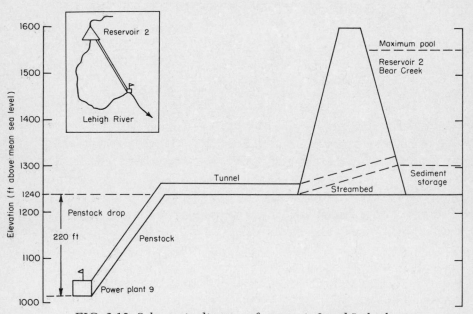

FIG. 2.12. Schematic diagram of reservoir 2 and Lehigh pipe.

able, subject to change from one simulation run to the next, but its value is likely to remain fixed at 0.85 over most trial designs, thereby reflecting the current highly developed and stable state of technology of turbine and generator design.

The following functions and constants are used in calculating the energy produced from reservoir releases. The energy equation is $E = KQhe$, where E is electric energy per unit time, K is a conversion factor, Q is flow per unit time, h is head, and e is a factor reflecting the efficiency of the turbines and generators. The factor K is a constant 0.1024 in the Lehigh simulation program; it is read as an input, and converts units of (10^2 acre-ft × ft) into megawatt-hours; Q is flow through the turbines in 10^2 acre-ft per month; h is average power head in feet; and e is the efficiency factor.

To compute energy production from water flows it is necessary to estimate the average head over the time period involved. For power plants 1 through 6, average reservoir contents for the month are computed by summing initial and final contents and dividing by 2; average heads associated with these contents are derived from the head-capacity functions for the six reservoirs shown in Fig. 2.10. Alternatively, one could compute the mean of initial and final heads, but this requires two references to the head-capacity functions.

Power plants 7 and 8 are fixed-head plants, so the average head is the maximum head for each. The average head at power plant 9 is the average head for reservoir 2 as computed above, plus the fixed head of the penstock. As shown in Fig. 2.12, this gross fixed head is 220 feet; assuming a 5 percent friction loss, the net effective fixed head is 209 feet.

Associated with plants 7 and 8 are pumping plants that lift water from reservoir 1 or 2 to the gravity channel shown in Fig. 2.11. The basic energy equation, $E = KQhe$ is again used to compute the pumping energy required. Pumping head varies with the contents of reservoir 1 or 2, and an average pumping head is computed by subtracting the head associated with reservoir contents from a base value of pumping head which represents the difference in elevations of the reservoir pool and the conveyance channel. As shown in Fig. 2.11, pumping head ranges from a maximum of 110 feet to a minimum of zero.

ESTABLISHING AN OPERATING PROCEDURE

The configuration of individual elements and the values of the design variables and the invariant functions, parameters and constants described above convey the essential information about the system whose behavior is to be simulated. The essence of simulation is to trace the behavior of the system over time, given certain initial conditions, inflows to the system, and a set of targets, release rules, and structural constraints. The rules for storing, releasing, and routing water through the system comprise an operating procedure. In general, reservoir storage for domestic and industrial water supply, irrigation, improvement of water quality, and hydroelectric power generation conflict to some extent with reservation of storage space for withholding or retarding flood waters. And reservoir drawdowns for all of these purposes conflict with the maintenance of reservoir levels for recreational use and power generation. It is evident that in a complex system there are many alternative policies for storing, releasing, routing, and pumping water so as to meet the targets.

Conceptually, there is associated with each system design an optimal operating policy; the optimal design, therefore, is predicated on its unique optimal policy. The derivation of this policy is likely to be impracticable, however, with existing analytic or simulation techniques; on the one hand, the formulations are intractable, while on the other hand, relatively few of the infinite number of possible policies can feasibly be tested. If, however, the essential parameters and decision variables of an operating policy can be varied along with other system inputs, many alternative policies can be tested without recoding the simulation, and an optimal policy can be approximated. Thus, our approach to the problem of obtaining an optimal operating policy involves the specification, as input data, of the relevant parameters of a generalized operating policy; this gain in flexibility is accompanied, however, by greater complexity in coding the simulation program.[29]

[29] For a more detailed discussion of operating procedures, see Maass, Hufschmidt, *et al*, reference 10, chap. 11.

The North Pacific Division, U. S. Army Corps of Engineers has been concerned with developing optimal operating policies for power generation in the Columbia River system of reservoirs and power plants. For a research paper on this problem, see R. J. Hanson, "Long-range regulation of a hydroelectric system with storage dams," An unpublished Master of Science Thesis submitted to Oregon State University (June 1962).

Operating the Lehigh system. The Lehigh simulation operates to provide specified minimum flows below each reservoir and to meet, insofar as possible (and subject to specified constraints), a target streamflow for water supply at Bethlehem and a target output of electric energy (at a specified load factor and with a specified monthly distribution) for the entire system. After minimum flows are provided, supplementary constrained releases are made to meet the water-supply target and then, if necessary, to meet the energy target. The constraints apply to flood-storage space and to minimum recreation storage at each reservoir. In terms of priorities, minimum flows and flood-storage space have absolute first priority; minimum recreation storage, second priority; water-supply output, third priority; and energy output, the lowest priority.

The first priority given to minimum flows is in accord with accepted practice of preventing complete dry-up of the stream if at all possible. Priority given to flood-storage space and recreation storage follows from the manner of dealing with these purposes — through constraints (maximum or minimum) on reservoir levels. Relative importance assigned to these purposes can be varied by changing the constraint levels. At one extreme, required flood-storage space and required recreation storage can be set to zero; at this extreme, they are not effective constraints on releases for water supply or energy. At the other extreme, flood control and recreation storage can be made so high as to absorb all available reservoir space. Priority assigned to water-supply output at the expense of energy output is justified by the fact that within broad limits energy deficits are less costly than deficits in water supply. The arbitrary nature of these priorities is mitigated by the existence of two recreation constraint levels which allows for considerable flexibility in operating policy.

Releases for water supply and energy are made first from reservoir 1 (or 2),[30] and then, if necessary, from reservoirs 3–6, according to an apportionment rule that attempts to equate, for each reservoir, the ratio of its vacant reservoir space to total vacant space for the system to the analogous ratio of expected reservoir inflows.

During flood periods, flows in excess of those which would cause damage are stored in the reservoirs to the extent possible. The basic unit of time for flood simulation and routing is three hours.

[30] Only one of these reservoirs can be present in any single design.

Under input option, the program provides for the simulation to be run for a specified number of years, to achieve a steady state, before recording the performance of the system in physical and economic terms.

CONSTRUCTING COST AND BENEFIT FUNCTIONS

At this point in the process of model preparation, sufficient information is available to allow a simulation program to be coded. The system is delineated, historical and operational hydrology are available in proper form, design variables and other parameters are developed, and an operating procedure is constructed. It should be possible to select values for the design variables and other parameters, to assume initial conditions of reservoir storage and other state variables, and to make a simulation run for the system. The results would be in physical terms only — stationary state probabilities of reservoir contents, releases from reservoirs, quantities of water provided at use points, and electric energy generated at the individual power plants. But there is no implicit or explicit way of evaluating, in economic terms, this spate of information on system performance. For this purpose we need data on the costs of resource inputs — dams, power plants, recreation facilities; and the benefits of system outputs — water supplies, electric energy, recreation visitation, and flood peak reductions.

Because we wish to scan a wide range of system designs, each of which includes reservoirs, power plants, recreational facilities, and system outputs, it is desirable to construct functions relating structures to their costs, and purposes to their benefits. In addition, we do not assume that a system must provide an assigned output — say, for water supply or electric energy — or that deficits be held within narrow limits. This follows (a) from the stochastic nature of hydrologic inputs which may occasion large deficits during a simulation run, and (b) from the objective of translating system performance into economic terms. Accordingly, rather large deficits are admissible; this requires that information be provided, for each system output, on the economic losses associated with such deficits. Thus, economic-loss functions join cost functions and long-run benefit functions as the indispensable tools for converting physical performance into economic payoff.

Cost functions. A functional relationship between cost and capacity exists for all relevant development measures, whether it be a dam, dike, tunnel, levee, powerhouse, campsite, or flood warning system. Standard methods of cost estimating can be applied to obtain a number of point estimates of capital and of operation, maintenance, and replacement (OMR) costs of designs to different scales; from these, a cost function can be constructed for each type of development measure. In some instances it is necessary to fit the data with a sequence of several functions, each of which governs a segment of the allowable range for the particular development measure.

To illustrate the general characteristics of cost functions, we cite examples from the Lehigh system. As shown in Table 2.5, sixteen of the system design variables are classed as development measures. These include facilities for storage (reservoirs), power, and recreation. In the following paragraphs we discuss the relevant cost-capacity functions for both capital and OMR costs.[31]

Cost of storage facilities. For any assumed dam design, the capital cost of the structure and reservoir is essentially the same, no matter what the purpose of the dam. Cost includes land-taking and clearing, relocations of structures and roads, the dam and its appurtenances, diking, access, and service facilities. Design and estimating procedures for dams and reservoirs are well established, and rapid improvements are currently being made, as computer technology is utilized increasingly for this task.[32] Our distinctive requirement is that enough cost estimates be made to give adequate coverage over the full range of this design variable.

The capital cost-capacity functions for the six Lehigh reservoirs, shown in Figs. 2.13 and 2.14, are typical for many storage reservoirs. Some costs are incurred before any capacity is realized, so the curves intercept slightly above the origin. The first increments of storage can typically be secured only at considerable cost, so the curves rise sharply; as the river valley broadens and the reservoir area increases with height of dam, the slopes decrease, indicating that incremental storage can now be obtained at reduced

---

[31] In the following discussion money costs and real costs are assumed to be identical. For cases where money and real costs may differ, see Maass, Hufschmidt, *et al.*, reference 10, chaps. 2 and 4.

[32] See, for example, R. M. Weaver, "Preliminary design of concrete dams by means of computers," Portland Cement Association, Chicago, Illinois (1963).

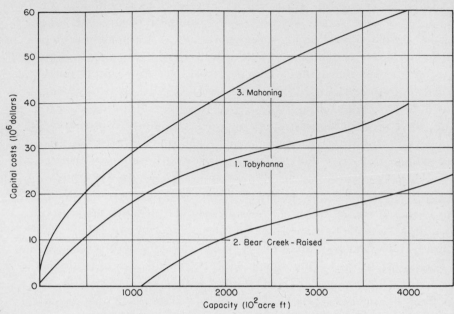

FIG. 2.13. Capital costs of reservoirs 1, 2, and 3.

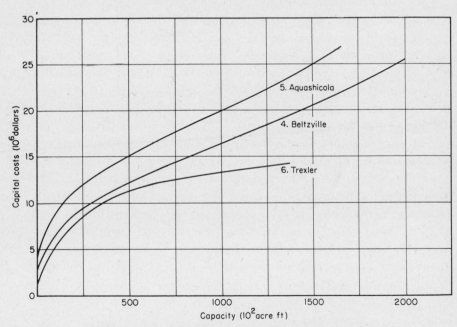

FIG. 2.14. Capital costs of reservoirs 4, 5, and 6.

increments of cost. At upper ranges of capacity the slopes again increase as more and more land must be acquired in the inundated area, as diking requirements are frequently encountered, and as extensive highway, railroad, and utility relocations become necessary.

An important question relates to the number of point estimates of cost that would be made to establish the function. Information gained from prior studies of the geology, topography, access, and materials availability of dam and reservoir sites and from preliminary dam designs should allow important cost discontinuities or sharp changes in slope to be spotted before detailed cost estimates are begun. When such anomolies are suspected, it will probably be necessary (a) to increase the number of point estimates over those normally required to identify a well-behaved function and (b) to give more intensive coverage to the range within which discontinuities or steep slopes are suspected. We can assume that, for well-behaved cost functions with no discontinuities or sharp changes in slope, the justification for more points drops rapidly after the first five or six estimates, if these are located to cover the full range of capacities. Thus in Fig. 2.13, a set of five points, at increments of 100,000 acre ft over the range from 0 to 400,000 acre ft, gives a reasonable representation of the functions for reservoirs 1 and 3. Five additional points, spotted (for maximum effectiveness) over the range of steepest slope, would provide significant new information, but much less than that gained from the first five points.

Cost of specific power facilities. Wherever streamflow and potential head are sufficient, a variety of hydroelectric power facilities may warrant consideration among the development measures in a river system design. In general, these facilities may be integral parts of the storage dam, adjacent to the storage dam, on canal drops, or at the outlet of long penstocks or tunnels several miles below the potential storage facilities.

Where power generation is the sole purpose at a storage site, or where only short-term pondage is required for run-of-river power production, the total cost of storage or pondage can be treated as a specific power cost. In many large multiplant, multipurpose development schemes, step-up switchyard, transmission, and step-down market substation costs are also treated as part of the capital costs attributed to power. Unlike the computation of costs for storage facilities, therefore, there is considerable variation in the composition of costs of power facilities from system to system.

The costs to be identified include land, powerhouse structures, penstocks, tunnels, conduits, turbines, forebays, afterbays, surge tanks, generators, electrical control equipment, service facilities, switchyard structures, transformers and associated equipment, transmission lines, and substations. Because of the highly advanced technology of power system design, the limited influence of geology and site topography on major electrical features, and the extensive experience and increasing standardization in power plant construction, it is common practice in estimating at-site power installation costs to use well-established unit cost functions, which relate costs per kilowatt to installed capacity. Such conventional unit power costs vary inversely with total installed capacity, size of unit, and power head because more power can be developed with a given flow as head increases and because economies of scale are achieved. Where an installation takes advantage of unique features of the terrain unrelated to the storage site, supplementary cost functions, which relate costs to the scale of diversion conveyances, penstocks, forebay storage, tailrace channels, and the like, are required.

The nine Lehigh power plants include conventional features plus a few unique characteristics. A power potential is assumed at each of the six storage sites, with the power structure assumed to be an integral part of the dam, and with penstocks assumed to be embedded in the storage structure in a manner consistent with standard design for small dams with power features. These are plants numbered 1–6 in Table 2.5. In addition, three power sites (numbered 7–9 in Table 2.5) are associated with long diversion tunnels from reservoirs 1 and 2. For the six at-site power installations, each of the family of unit-cost curves, one for each size of unit, relates unit cost to power head, as shown in Fig. 2.15.[33] Because of the variability of penstock design under different dam designs and proposed operating characteristics of the power units, penstock costs are omitted from these power cost curves. Instead, a subsidiary cost function developed for our purposes and shown in

[33] These cost functions, developed by the Federal Power Commission, draw on a considerable body of statistics on hydro construction.

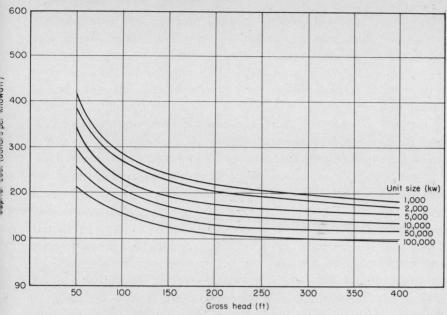

FIG. 2.15. Unit capital cost of hydroelectric power plant as a function of gross head, for units of various sizes.

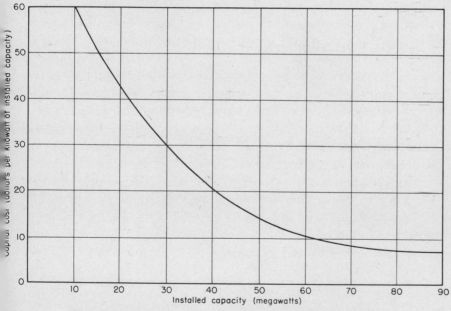

FIG. 2.16. Unit capital cost of penstock, power plants 1–6.

Fig. 2.16 relates unit costs of steel-lined, concrete penstocks embedded in earth dams to installed capacity. While the cost functions of Figs. 2.15 and 2.16 are in terms of unit power costs for any selected unit size and power head, the computer program converts unit costs to total capital costs for the particular design variable under study.

For power plants at the outlets of the "Beltzville pipe" and "Lehigh pipe" diversions, separate calculations are required to account for the diversion tunnels, forebay pondage, penstocks, and tailrace channels. A group of subsidiary curves encompassing the required range of sizes for each feature are consolidated in the unit-cost curves in Figs. 2.17 and 2.18.

Capital costs for switchyards and transmission lines are excluded. The entire planning area is presently served by a highly developed and completely interconnected network of electric transmission facilities; any power which might be developed in the Lehigh system would constitute a minor portion of total power capacity of the area, and would necessarily be integrated with the existing electric system and operated in a manner dictated by that system rather than as a separate source. Under such circumstances, transmission extensions to the source of hydro power and switching facilities at the sites would be added only to the extent necessary to integrate hydro power output with the predominantly thermal power supply of the area.

Cost of specific recreation facilities. In contrast to the well-documented literature in hydroelectric power investment costs, there is substantially less experience and standardization in estimating costs for recreation facilities incorporated into water-resource developments. With the recent increasing emphasis in the United States on recreation as a major purpose of water-resource developments, recreation specialists are gaining greater experience in developing and applying techniques for selection, design, and estimating costs of facilities in a variety of environments.[34]

Water-based recreation requires site developments and struc-

[34] *Outdoor recreation for America,* Report of U. S. Outdoor Recreation Resources Review Commission (Government Printing Office, Washington, 1962); *Handbook for reservoir planning,* U. S. National Park Service (Government Printing Office, Washington, 1960).

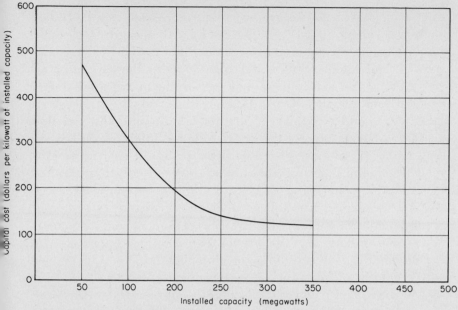

FIG. 2.17. Unit capital cost of auxiliary power facilities, reservoirs 1 and 2, power plants 7 and 8 (Beltzville pipe).

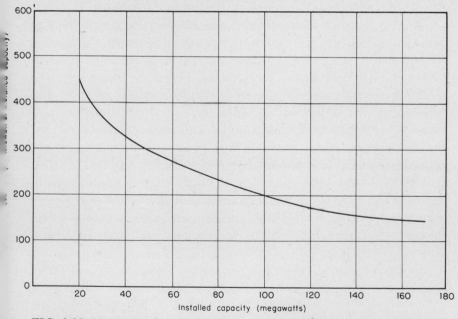

FIG. 2.18. Unit capital cost of auxiliary power facilities, reservoir 1, power plant 9 (Lehigh pipe).

tures such as access roads, trails, parking areas, camp sites, utilities, shoreline improvements, and boating and bathing facilities. Potential sites for recreation development differ markedly in the composition and intensity of capital improvements that would be appropriate for the site. Important factors are the makeup and degree of local and regional demands, climate, seasonality, alternative facilities available, terrain, shoreline slope and configuration, access, and other uses of the water resource. Moreover, each site may possess a unique design capacity, or set of such capacities, related to the mix of associated investments in recreation facilities, despite existing and projected needs of the service or market area. The key to optimal planning of recreation investments, therefore, is careful adjustment between estimates of demand and the potentialities and limitations of the site for recreation development.

Traditionally, water-resource development measures are planned with emphasis on purposes such as water supply, irrigation, flood control, and electric power. Only after a design is fixed on this basis is recreation considered as a purpose of the plan. Annual visitor-day (and more recently camper-day) estimates for fixed levels of reservoir development are made, followed by estimates of facilities required to accommodate these demands and by adjustments to account for limitations on design capacity reflecting the deterioration of quality with overcrowding. Capital costs of this recreation plan are finally calculated. Only recently has this procedure been modified to take recreation more explicitly into account in initial formulation of a water-resource plan.[35]

In contrast to the traditional method, our approach in establishing the Lehigh simulation program is to treat recreation as an equal purpose so that estimates of visitor-day attendance and costs of needed recreational facilities are required over the full range of facility sizes. Thus it is necessary to construct for each development a function relating maximum recreation attendance, say in visitor-days per year, to the scale of the development — say, size of storage reservoir (which in turn implies the length of shoreline). In essence, this is a recreation capacity–storage capacity function with a given or assumed level of associated investment in recreational

[35] See *Outdoor recreation for America*, reference 34, and *Policies, standards and procedures in the formulation, evaluation and review of plans for use and development of water and related resources*, Report of the President's Water Resources Council, Sen. Doc. 97, 87th Cong., 2d sess.

facilities. It is also necessary to construct functions that relate unit (per visitor-day) capital cost of recreation facilities to the level of recreation attendance. Because scale economies are likely to exist, it is not adequate to assume a constant unit cost of investment independent of attendance.

For each of the six reservoirs of the Lehigh system we develop a function relating maximum annual recreation attendance, in visitor-days per surface acre of reservoir pool, to reservoir storage. These functions are shown in Fig. 2.19. They are derived from a generalized relationship of unit attendance to reservoir storage developed by the National Park Service from historical attendance data at 90 Corps of Engineers reservoirs located throughout the country.[36] We adjust the relationship to fit the particular recreation conditions (quality and accessibility) at each of the six Lehigh sites. By using these functions and the functions relating reservoir area to reservoir capacity, estimates of maximum annual recreation at-

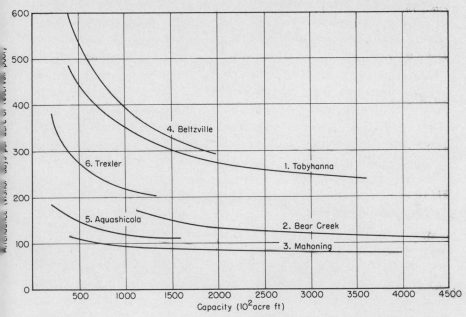

FIG. 2.19. Unit annual recreation attendance as a function of reservoir capacity, reservoirs 1–6.

[36] Obtained from the Philadelphia Regional Office, National Park Service. An analogous function was used in the Corps of Engineers Delaware River basin survey; see *Delaware River basin*, reference 1, vol. XI, p. W–43.

tendance, or recreation capacity, can be obtained for any level of reservoir storage at these sites.

Unit costs of recreation facilities generally decrease with scale of development; the Lehigh simulation program can handle both variable and constant unit-cost functions. While a single cost-attendance function is specified for all Lehigh reservoirs, it may be necessary in other analyses to construct a separate function for each reservoir to reflect unique costs of land acquisition and development and access to the recreation sites.

Cost of operation, maintenance, and replacement of facilities. Included in this category are the continuing costs incurred for operating personnel—dam-tenders, ditchriders, power plant operators, flood forecasters, communications technicians—the cost of labor, supplies and materials for maintenance of structures and equipment, recurring engineering and administrative costs, and costs of major replacement of facilities. Operation and maintenance costs tend to vary little from year to year, but costs of major replacements are non-uniform and are high in later years as equipment wears out. For convenience all OMR costs are converted to average annual values spread equally over the economic life of the system.

Experience in actual operation of water-resource systems provides well-documented statistical information for most OMR costs. However, the increasing trend toward semiautomatic or fully automatic operation by remote control of many major installations—particularly power plants—is not generally reflected in historical data on OMR costs. The impact of these advanced techniques on reducing future operating costs should be taken into account when OMR cost functions are constructed.

OMR cost functions are constructed for the reservoirs, power plants, and recreational facilities of the Lehigh system, using data from the Corps of Engineers on the Delaware River basin. In computing the OMR cost function for reservoirs, annual operation and maintenance costs are assumed to be functions solely of capital costs; replacement costs are added in the form of an annual value, computed as a fixed percentage of capital costs. The composite function of OMR costs versus capital costs of storage, used for all six Lehigh reservoirs, is shown in Fig. 2.20.

Power-operating charges are expressed as annual costs per kilowatt of installed capacity, that is, as a direct function of the number

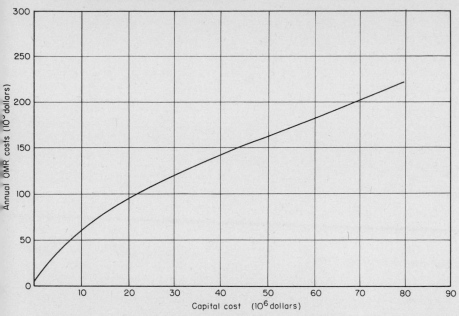

FIG. 2.20. Annual OMR cost as a function of capital cost, reservoirs 1–6.

and size of units, and are only indirectly related to total capital cost. This is consistent with Federal Power Commission practice, and the results are readily convertible to total operation and maintenance costs. The annual interim replacement component is expressed as a composite percentage of investment in powerhouse, penstock, machinery, and the like. For simplicity it is desirable to have a combined expression of power OMR costs, but unit capital costs per kilowatt of capacity vary considerably with head, as shown in the family of capital cost curves, Fig. 2.13. As a practical matter, studies of near-optimal designs are presumed to deal with a fairly narrow range of rated heads and installed capacities, so we find it reasonable to treat interim replacement costs by adding a fixed annual cost per unit of capacity to the operation and maintenance cost function. The resulting OMR cost function, applicable to all nine power plants of the Lehigh system, is shown in Fig. 2.21.

The OMR costs for recreation are assumed to be proportional to capital costs. A review of the basic data and procedures used by the National Park Service in the Delaware River study reveals that annual operation and maintenance and an assumed replacement of one third of capital facilities every 25 years requires a total

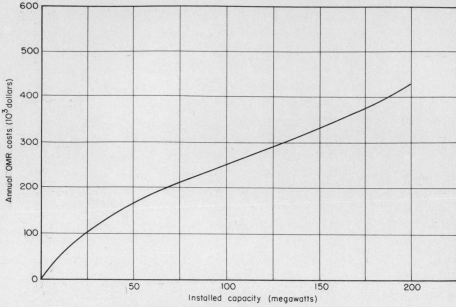

FIG. 2.21. Annual OMR cost, power plants 1–9.

annual OMR allowance of 2.9 percent of capital cost. In general, refinements in OMR estimates for recreation facilities which reflect decreasing unit costs with increasing scale of development may be warranted.

BENEFIT FUNCTIONS

In an earlier section we described design variables relating to system outputs and gave examples of these for the Lehigh system. Here we deal with the benefit functions associated with system outputs; that is, we evaluate the benefits that attach to various levels of water supply (for irrigation, domestic or industrial use), electric energy, recreation attendance, reduction of flood flows, and increase of low flows.

To be useful for simulation analysis benefit functions take on a special form. As with cost functions, we require more than a point estimate of the unit (or total) value of a specified level of output; instead, we require a set of estimated benefit values associated with a range of target outputs. In addition, our benefit function combines two elements: (1) the values associated with each target output level, or those benefits which accrue when the system produces exactly a specified annual output, and (2) the values associated with (a) failures to meet target outputs and with (b) over-fulfillment of targets in any time period. Thus an economic loss is sustained when the system incurs a deficit, while an economic gain is realized when excess output is produced. Figure 2.22 presents an example of such a two-element benefit function. Segment A shows the relation between planned or target output and total benefits for a specified period, say one year. Segments B_1 and B_2 are interpreted as follows: For a planned or target output of x, with benefits of $\bar{y}$, deficits in physical output are penalized according to segment B_1 of the function, and surpluses are credited according to segment B_2. The slopes of segments B_1 and B_2 reflect actual experience with hydro power systems. The rate of loss (the slope of function B_1) is greater than the rate of change of the "long-run" function A, because unanticipated output deficits in an existing system are more costly than a reduction in planned output level. Conversely, the rate of gain from surpluses (the slope of function B_2) is smaller than that of function A, again because unanticipated surpluses in an established system have less value than an increase in planned output level. In other words, using energy as an example, dump power is less valuable than firm power.

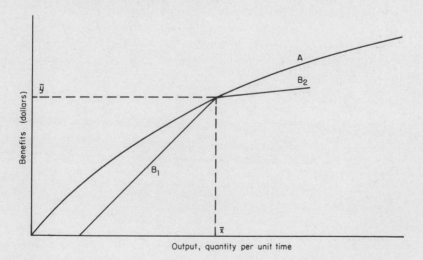

FIG. 2.22. Two-element benefit function: element A shows benefits as a function of target output per unit time; element B_1–B_2 shows benefits as a function of attained outputs when target output is $\bar{x}$.

The long-run benefit function is familiar from the literature on water-resource planning and economic evaluation.[37] Construction of the function for use in simulation is thus subject to the usual conceptual and measurement problems associated with economic evaluation of water-resource developments. We do not deal with these problems in any detail here, but it is important to stress the unique role that benefit functions play in system design. We are concerned with them as means of plan formulation—measures which lead to the optimal design—rather than as tools for justification of investment after the design is formulated, or as means for allocating costs among purposes.[38]

As means for formulating optimal designs, benefit functions should measure the lesser of two values: (1) the resource cost of providing equivalent goods and services by the least costly alternative means external to the system, where alternative cost is measured on the same basis as system cost, or (2) willingness of consumers to pay for the goods and services. For the case where costs of the external alternative are less than willingness to pay, we can assume that the external alternative would be undertaken in the absence of any system development. In this case there would be resource savings (or losses) arising from undertaking the development rather than the external alternative. These savings or losses constitute the net benefits (positive or negative) of the undertaking for formulation purposes. Where costs of the external alternative exceed willingness to pay, it is axiomatic that the external alternative would not be undertaken in the absence of the project, and willingness to pay becomes the proper measure of benefits for formulation purposes.[39]

[37] See the literature cited in Maass, Hufschmidt, *et al.*, reference 10, p. 1.

[38] Benefit functions have a legitimate use in cost allocation studies, but the concept of benefits used for this purpose will, in general, differ from the concept used in system design. See M. M. Hufschmidt, J. V. Krutilla, and J. Margolis, "Standards and criteria for formulating and evaluating Federal water resources developments," Report of Panel of Consultants to the Bureau of the Budget (1961).

[39] For cases in which cost of the external alternative is the relevant measure, see P. O. Steiner, "The role of alternative cost in project design and selection," *QJE* 79, 417 (August 1965).

A somewhat different approach is presented in Sen. Doc. 97. The lesser of the value derived from willingness-to-pay or the value derived from alternative cost (measured in terms of non-federal financing) is used to construct benefit functions; but an additional test is imposed: for a development (or an increment of development) to be acceptable, its cost must be no greater than the cost of its alternative, with costs measured on the same basis. In most cases the two approaches yield the same result, but that presented here is more straightforward and will always lead to an unambiguous result.

See also Hufschmidt, Krutilla, and Margolis, reference 38, pp. 41–46, and Maass, Hufschmidt, *et al.*, reference 10, p. 215.

In the following sections we present long-run benefit functions for typical water-resource system outputs, derived, in part, from data in the Corps of Engineers Delaware Basin Report. Discussion is directed to the specific form of benefit function required for simulation analysis, and to the problems of data manipulation associated with constructing functions of such form.

Benefit functions for municipal and industrial water supply. A starting point for construction of a benefit function for water supply is a definition of water-supply output in specific and unambiguous terms; this requires a four-dimensional specification—quantity, quality, point, or points, of use, and time distribution. Thus, for the Lehigh, water-supply output is defined as an assured flow of acceptable quality in the river channel at Bethlehem, with a cyclic pattern of mean monthly flow rates. For example, an assured mean annual flow rate of 100 cfs would have rates varying from 92 cfs in the winter months to 108 cfs in the summer months, according to the monthly distribution shown in Table 2.6.[40]

It is helpful to construct an aggregate demand function for water supply or, as in Fig. 2.23, a set of such functions spanning the period of economic analysis, which relate quantity of water demanded by domestic and industrial users to price. The shape of the curves in Fig. 2.23 reflects the low elasticity of demand for water over a considerable range of price.

In an aggregate demand function combining both domestic and industrial demands, the demand is relatively inelastic for basic domestic supplies—represented by the segment SS', Fig. 2.23. Demands for commercial and industrial supplies are likely to be more elastic, as shown by the segment S'R of the function. When the zone of saturation of demand is reached, the function becomes highly inelastic; relatively little additional water is demanded even as the price falls to zero.

Unfortunately, data required for constructing aggregate demand functions for water supply are meager. In practice, it is usually possible to make only a single point estimate of demand (such as point Q in Fig. 2.23) for any specified date during the period of economic analysis. Associated with this estimate is an assumption that the price to be paid by users lies in the demand saturation zone, a

[40] Specification of an assured rate of flow at a single point as in this example is usually a simplified statement of a complex of water withdrawals and returns along the stream. To be meaningful, the stated rate of flow must meet a specified pattern of flow rates (with water of acceptable quality) at various points along the stream. Often, a single critical demand rate (for a large city or a major industrial plant) will dominate; that is, when this demand is met, all other demands along the stream will also be met. In other cases no such simple rule will suffice.

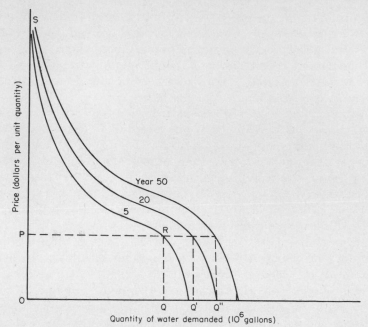

FIG. 2.23. Aggregate demand function for domestic and industrial water supply.

highly inelastic segment of the curve. In the Lehigh basin, for example, such point estimates of water-supply demand at Bethlehem are made for the years 1965, 1980, and 2000.

An improvement over single point estimates of demand is the computation of ranges of demand, using different price assumptions. This may be undertaken where industrial uses comprise a major part of the demand, and the feasibility and cost of water-saving alternatives such as recirculation can be determined. At prices approaching the cost of water-saving alternatives, water-supply demands can be expected to decline sharply.

Recognizing that the exact shape of the demand function is largely unknown, we suggest the following approach as a practical expedient:

1. On the basis of the prevailing price structure for water, estimate the total quantity of water to be demanded—such as Point Q in Fig. 2.23. (This is essentially the method commonly used today.)

2. Estimate costs of water-saving measures and equipment for the commercial and industrial sectors, and translate these costs into unit values—dollars/mgd, for example.

3. Assume that this unit cost establishes the point, or zone, of inflection of the aggregate demand function, such that this point

(*R* in Fig. 2.23) represents the highest unit price, *P*, consistent with the estimated demand, *Q*, of Fig. 2.23. At prices significantly above *P*, the demand would decline sharply, because water-saving measures are taken by industry and commercial establishments. This expedient invokes the simplifying assumption that the demand function is perfectly inelastic between the prevailing unit prices and the imputed price of water-saving measures. Given the uncertainties involved in estimates of water demands, this assumption is reasonable.

4. Compute total value of the estimated demand, *Q*, by multiplying by the threshhold price, *P*. This value is equivalent to the area *OPRQ* in Fig. 2.23. We can now safely assume that willingness-to-pay benefits for the estimated demand are *at least* equal to *P·Q*: this total value is shown as point *D* in Fig. 2.24.

5. Assume that the threshhold price *P* measures the value to all quantities of water up to the estimated demand *Q*; this is equivalent to drawing the straight line *OD* in Fig. 2.24. We can be sure that willingness-to-pay benefits are at least equal to benefits computed in this way, and, in general, exceed them; thus a lower limit is established for willingness-to-pay benefits for all levels of water supply output from zero to the estimated total demand. In Fig. 2.24, curve *OD* establishes the lower limit of curve *OB*.

6. Compute the cost of supplying several levels of water-supply output by the least costly means external to the system, using the

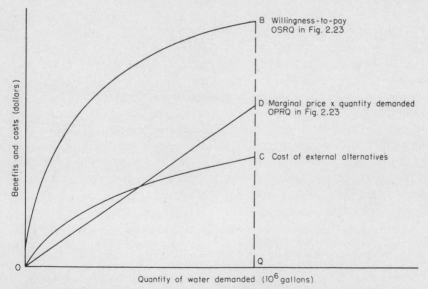

FIG. 2.24. Benefit functions for domestic and industrial water supply.

same interest rate and price assumptions as for system costs and making the appropriate adjustments for differences in water transport costs. This establishes a function such as OC in Fig. 2.24, which represents costs avoided and which, under certain conditions, can be used as a measure of water-supply benefits.

7. To test whether the alternative cost function can be used as a measure of benefits, determine if it lies below that function established by multiplying unit price by quantity. In Fig. 2.24, we ask if curve OC lies below curve OD. If so, it is reasonable to assume, for any level of output, that the external alternative would be undertaken in the absence of development for water supply; the cost of the external alternative is therefore saved by developing water supply within the system, and this saving becomes the relevant benefit measure to be used in formulation.

If alternative costs are greater than the product of quantity and marginal price associated with the demand estimates, the role of the cost function in formulation becomes questionable. It is mandatory to compare points on the alternative cost function with their counterparts on the willingness-to-pay function — OB in Fig. 2.24. Such comparisons are approximate at best because good data on willingness to pay are scarce. In any event, alternative cost estimates that greatly exceed the product of quantity and marginal price are questionable because their bases — estimates of consumer surplus — are usually of low reliability.

Care must be used in defining the relevant alternative to be sure that it is actually external to the system under study. Thus, for two alternatives, say, reservoirs A and B within a system, it is not correct to consider the costs of reservoir B as the measure of benefits of reservoir A, and vice versa. Cost comparisons of alternatives within a system provide information on the least-cost design, but tell nothing about the cost of alternatives that would be undertaken in the absence of system development. In general, no matter how large the system, there will always be some external alternative, and the cost of external alternatives should be evaluated to determine the extent of resource savings or losses that would occur if development of an external alternative were precluded by a development within the system.[41]

[41] Definition of the relevant system for planning is to some extent arbitrary and is affected by political and institutional factors. The current trend is to expand the definition of water-resource system to include many development alternatives formerly considered outside the system as defined by U. S. Federal water-resource agencies. For an example in the field of water supply and water quality, see A. V. Kneese, *The economics of regional water quality management* (The Johns Hopkins Press, Baltimore, 1964), chap. 6.

For the Lehigh system, point estimates of water-supply demand were made by the Corps of Engineers for the years 1965, 1980, and 2010. These are analogous to points Q, Q', and Q'' in Fig. 2.23. However, the functions in Fig. 2.24 were not computed in the Corps survey; instead, calculations of alternative costs were made, based on historical cost data (adjusted to current prices) not specifically related to external alternatives. In the absence of cost data on external alternatives, we use, as input to the simulation analysis, the constant annual cost of $8,800 per cfs; this is derived from historical data and represents the best estimate of the unit cost of water supply from external alternatives. Reliance on this single value for all levels of demand is tantamount to use of a linear function between points O and C, Fig. 2.24.

An alternative approach skirts the problem of direct estimation of benefits in terms of willingness-to-pay. In lieu of a benefit function for water supply, the projected water-supply demands establish constraints which are respected in the search for an optimal system design. The assumption implicit in this approach is that meeting the water demands is worth doing. This assumption is usually made by planners when water demands are estimated or projected. An approximate test of the assumption in formulating a multipurpose system is the extent to which total system benefits, exclusive of a water-supply benefit component, fall short of total system costs. A judgment must then be made to ascertain whether water supply is worth at least the excess costs. A more conclusive test is to determine the opportunity costs, in terms of benefits for other purposes foregone, of providing a given increment of water supply. This cost can be found by setting the water-supply target somewhat under the projected demands, say at 80 and 90 percent of demand, and increasing other targets. Progressive gains in net benefits resulting from use of facilities for purposes other than water supply reveal these incremental costs (benefits foregone), and thus provide evidence which policy-makers can use to decide whether or not to accept the water-supply constraint. For example, if a 10 percent reduction in target outputs for water supply and a consequent increase in target outputs for other purposes reveal an unusually high response in increase of system benefits for other purposes, policy-makers might conclude that supplying the last 10 percent of water is not worth the cost in benefits that would have to be foregone.

Benefit functions for hydroelectric power. Specific external alternatives for hydroelectric power are readily identifiable in the form of fuel-fired generating stations in most areas, and data are plentiful on the cost of these alternative opportunities. The value of power to users—the willingness-to-pay concept—is applied only in exceptional cases, and the computations of benefit measures in alternative cost terms are normally quite straightforward.

The value of hydroelectric power is usually expressed in terms of two components: first, a capacity value representing the fixed elements of cost of the alternative power supply, and second, an energy value representing the variable costs of generation—predominantly fuel costs—of the alternative. These values are customarily expressed in dollars per kilowatt of capacity and mills per kilowatt-hours of energy, respectively.

Certain characteristics of hydroelectric power and thermal alternatives render value computations difficult; many factors influence the determination of hydroelectric power value from cost of thermal alternatives. These include improvements in technological efficiency of thermal production over time, variations in operating flexibility and in-service availability between thermal and hydroelectric plants, energy cost differentials between hydroelectric and thermal plants when their annual plant factors are not the same, and differences in the cost of transmitting power to the market.

Construction of a hydroelectric power benefit function for the Lehigh system reflects these complexities. The Lehigh area power requirements are served by a major utility of the eastern United States, which is interconnected at several points with other power systems in the Delaware River basin and in adjacent regions, and in turn with large utility complexes along the entire Eastern Seaboard. Together they form a huge integrated power supply and transmission complex with several million kilowatts of capacity. This capacity is predominantly steam-electric ranging from new, large, efficient units which serve as base-load producers, to old, high-cost units now relegated to a standby role. There is some hydroelectric capacity in the system, used primarily for peaking. Pumped storage peaking installations have been considered for the system at a number of sites and one large installation is under construction (1964). The transmission network is intensively developed, and additional high-voltage interconnections are planned.

Projected demands for power within transmission distance of the Lehigh area are far in excess of the hydro potential, and a preponderance of large-unit, large-station thermal supply is indicated for the foreseeable future. Demands are mainly of the urban-commercial-industrial class, and distribution of energy is through privately owned facilities; public bodies and cooperatives represent a minor portion of total load.

For our Lehigh simulation studies no restrictions are placed on the use of energy from the system in the existing power supply area. While power system characteristics definitely favor use of energy for peaking, this is not assumed in advance. Instead, the full range of possible uses, from peaking to base-load operation, is considered.

In seeking least-cost external alternatives to hydroelectric plant designs over the full range of plant factors, we recognize that changing technology is certain to alter the many variables which influence cost relationships of thermal and hydroelectric power over time. Large new steam-electric units, conventionally coal-fired or nuclear, would normally provide the alternative for base-load or system-load factor operation. For certain system characteristics, peak loads can be carried by steam units specifically designed for peaking, by gas turbines, diesel engines, or pumped storage capacity. Lacking the data essential for complete analysis of all these alternatives, particularly with respect to rapidly changing technology, we simplify the computations by basing alternative costs on large-scale steam-electric units only. The customary two-part capacity and energy benefit expression is consolidated into a single value, in mills-per-kilowatt-hour, by spreading the capacity component over the hours per month that the capacity is demanded and by adding this unit value to the energy value. Values computed in this way and actual peaking costs shown in cost statistics of the Federal Power Commission reveal a close similarity.

In order that estimates of alternative costs be comparable to estimates of system costs, capital and OMR costs of external alternatives are computed for ten interest rates—the rates used in the simulation program to discount all costs and benefits to present value terms. For simplicity, transmission cost adjustments and capacity-value adjustments which reflect differences in operating flexibility between hydroelectric and thermal plants are ignored. In computing thermal plant costs, a thermal efficiency of 9600 btu per net kilowatt-hour and a fuel cost of 36 cents per million btu are adopted. From these computations a family of functions is derived, one function for each interest rate, relating unit hydroelectric power values to plant factors, as shown in Fig. 2.25. For plant factors below 20 percent, the relevant external alternative is generally not a conventional thermal plant but is more likely to be a pumped-storage hydroelectric plant (for large systems) or gas turbine (for small systems); because cost data for these alternatives were not available in the Delaware basin study, the family of functions is not extended to this range of very low plant factors.

A typical long-run benefit function for power based on the alternative-cost concept is shown in Fig. 2.26. Definition of the function requires selection of a discount rate and a plant capacity factor. Curve *OB*, the long-run benefit function in Fig. 2.26, is analogous to curve *OC*, the comparable function for water supply in Fig. 2.24.

System load duration curves for the power market area reveal a distinctly fluctuating seasonal pattern in use of peaking capacity.

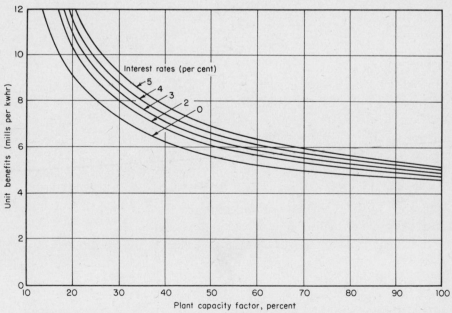

FIG. 2.25. Unit firm hydroelectric power benefits and hydroelectric plant capacity factor for various interest rates, using the cost of external alternative (thermal plant) as a measure of benefits.

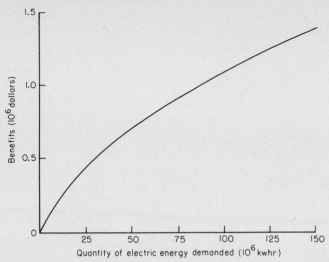

FIG. 2.26. Benefit function for firm hydroelectric power using the alternative cost measure with discount rate of 2.5 percent and plant factor of 20 percent.

For the range of plant factors considered, the monthly distributions of annual energy requirements shown in Table 2.6 were adopted.

While external alternatives to hydroelectric power development can readily be assumed for highly developed, industrialized economies, this may not be the case in less developed regions or countries. Some measurement of demand in response to a range of prices and over time would be necessary in such areas, as discussed above in connection with willingness to pay for municipal and industrial water supply. Projection of future demands for power is further complicated by the stimulus to economic development of the advent of large blocks of power to otherwise low power-consuming areas.[42]

Benefit functions for recreation. On page 51 we show how recreation-use capacity of a reservoir site in terms of annual visitor-days can be related to reservoir capacity. Here we are concerned with relating benefits to visitor-days of recreation attendance.

A visitor-day of recreation attendance is obviously not a homogenous unit; swimming, boating, fishing, picnicking, hiking, camp-

[42] A wealth of detail relating to electric power demands, supply patterns, and changing technology is contained in *National power survey*, a report by the Federal Power Commission, pts. I and II (Government Printing Office, 1964).

ing, and sightseeing are some of the activities covered in the term "recreation attendance at reservoirs." The composition of recreation attendance depends, in turn, on the recreation facilities provided and on the estimated demand for the types of recreation at the reservoir. Taking these characteristics into account, there follows a feasible means of deriving benefit functions analogous to those for water supply and hydroelectric power.

1. From projections of population, income, and leisure time, estimate the gross recreation demand by types of recreation services for the geographic area associated with the system. These demand estimates are analogous to the demand estimates for water supply discussed above and illustrated in Fig. 2.25. As for water supply and power, point estimates of demand imply certain assumptions or determinations as to price, which are based either on existing pricing policy for public recreation facilities, or, preferably, on studies of recreation demand schedules.

2. Compare the magnitudes of these demand estimates with estimates of system capacity for the several types of recreation services.

3. If estimated demands are significantly above system capacity for all types, we can assume that the entire output of recreation services of the system would be used, and that, in the absence of system facilities to provide this output, external alternatives would be developed. In this case it is appropriate to use the cost of the least expensive external alternative as the relevant measure of benefits. Functions such as OC in Fig. 2.24 could be constructed, relating costs of external alternatives to recreation capacity, and the derived costs would be compared to the assumed marginal willingness to pay (or threshhold price). As for water supply and power, costs of alternatives must be computed on the same basis as costs of system developments, and care must be used to insure that alternatives are truly external to the system.

4. Costs of external alternatives can be used to evaluate recreation outputs (in visitor-days per year for the various types of recreation services) only up to the level of estimated demands. Thus, where estimated demands are less than total system capacity, such excess capacity would have significantly less value, and in extreme cases, zero value.

5. Where the costs of external alternatives exceed the product of

the estimated demand and the assumed threshhold or marginal price, alternative cost may not be the relevant measure of benefits. It is then necessary to construct a benefit function in willingness-to-pay terms, if only in approximate form, and to apply the lesser of the values—that is, alternative cost or willingness to pay.[43]

In the Lehigh system, the estimates of current recreation demand for all types of outdoor recreation are far larger than the recreation capacity that could be provided by full development of reservoirs. Alternative cost is thus the relevant measure of benefits for formulation. In lieu of more refined analyses, we use for each reservoir in the Lehigh simulation program a composite cost of $1.05 per visitor-day for providing equivalent water-based recreation services. This value is based on a Corps of Engineers study of cost experience of public park agencies in the region. Although in this case the composite cost serves as a substitute at all reservoirs for costs of individual types of recreation services, and is used over the full range of recreation output, it would be preferable to examine alternative costs of each type of recreation individually, and to compute alternative costs for several scales of recreation development. In fact, our simulation program is designed to handle these more complex alternative-cost functions at each reservoir.

The preceding discussion deals only with annual attendance, but in reality recreation use is highly variable during the year. The degree of variability differs for each area depending on its location and on the type of outdoor recreation which the plan is intended to provide. In the Lehigh, the monthly distribution of annual recreation attendance at reservoirs, estimated by the National Park Service, is weighted heavily to the summer months, as shown in Table 2.7. From this distribution, it is manifest that system operation should strive to maintain reservoir pools at favorable recreation levels during the summer season of peak usage.

Benefit functions for irrigation. While irrigation is not a major purpose in the Delaware basin plan, it is often a dominant aspect of water-resource development. We need, therefore, to develop the essential framework for its consideration in system analysis by

---

[43] There is an extensive and rapidly growing literature on measurement of benefits for outdoor recreation. For citations of significant reports, see L. Merewitz, "Recreational benefits of water-resource development" (Harvard Water Program, June 1964) and J. L. Knetsch, "Economics of including recreation as a purpose of Eastern water projects," *JFE, 46,* 1148 (December 1964).

TABLE 2.7. Monthly distribution of annual recreation attendance (percent), Lehigh River basin

January	2.0	July	37.0
February	2.5	August	32.0
March	2.5	September	7.0
April	2.0	October	2.5
May	3.5	November	2.0
June	5.0	December	2.0

simulation, even though it does not appear as an explicit project purpose in our program.

In theory, estimating the value of water for the production of crops does not differ from estimating its value for industrial production of municipal and domestic services. In each case, the commodity is water of suitable quality, delivered to the point of use at the required time. Requirements for irrigation water are influenced by a host of variables: climate, amount and distribution of rainfall, soil, crops and cropping patterns, growing season, and effectiveness of farm management are but a few. Also, target (long-run) requirements are fixed by planners when selecting the area to be irrigated and the crops to be grown.

There are usually no external alternatives at reasonable cost, so that in the absence of the development it is infeasible to provide equivalent quantities of water to the irrigable area. Hence some measurement of willingness to pay is usually necessary in determining the value of irrigation water.

Direct irrigation benefits are defined as increases in net farm income resulting from the application of water, such increases being derived from determinations of the differences in farm incomes with and without the project.[44] These expected changes in net incomes are taken to represent "the maximum amounts which the farmers would be willing to pay if they were perfectly rational entrepreneurs."[45] To enforce higher payments would, of course, destroy incentive to settle irrigated lands. In practice, the willingness to pay is considerably less than increases in net farm income, as any repayment contract negotiation would reveal.

[44] U. S. Bureau of Reclamation *Instructions,* Ser. 110, Project Planning (September 1959).

[45] O. Eckstein, *Water-resource development, the economics of project evaluation* (Harvard University Press, Cambridge, 1958) p. 197.

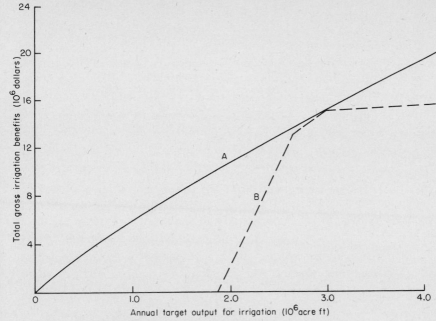

FIG. 2.27. Gross irrigation benefit function.

An aggregate demand function, a long-run benefit function, and a loss function, similar in form to those of Fig. 2.22, can be constructed for irrigation. It is important to specify in each case just where in the irrigation sequence the water is valued, for its value will be different at the point of diversion from what it is at the point of delivery into the farmers' turn-outs. (An analogous situation prevails in evaluating at-site, as distinct from delivered, electrical energy.) There is an extensive literature on the conceptual and empirical aspects of estimating the value of irrigation water.[46]

The form of the benefit function required for simulation is discussed in an earlier study,[47] where a unit benefit function, developed for irrigation water delivered to the farmers' lands, ranges from about $6.50 per acre foot annually for very low target output levels to about $4.50 per acre foot annually for large targets. Although specific values vary from project to project, the range of values indicates the nature of a typical irrigation benefit function. The unit values derived from studies of individual cases may be

[46] Eckstein, reference 45, chap. VII.
[47] Maass, Hufschmidt, *et al.*, reference 10, pp. 274–275.

transformed into a total gross benefit function, as in curve A, Fig. 2.27.

Flood-control benefits. Simulation analysis of flood situations yields information on flood peaks at points or zones of damage, both under unregulated conditions and as affected by system operation. The reductions in peak flows constitute the measure of physical performance, or flood-control output, of the system. Here we are concerned with measurement of benefits associated with reductions in peak flows; these are derived by subtracting from flood damages associated with unregulated peak flows those damages associated with regulated flows.

The economic damages associated with flood flows are derived by establishing, for each damage zone along the stream: (1) a stage-discharge function which relates the height of the water to the magnitude of the discharge, and (2) a damage-stage function, which relates economic losses to the height of the water, or river stage.

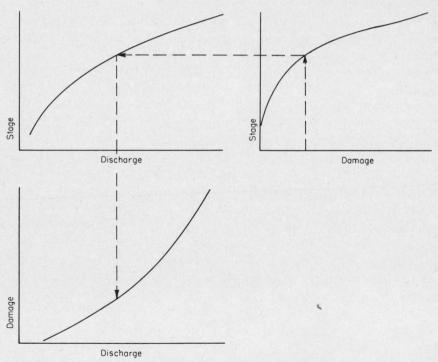

FIG. 2.28. Derivation of flood damage–discharge function from stage-discharge and flood damage–stage functions.

Combining these functions, as shown in Fig. 2.28, we develop a damage–discharge function which can be used directly in the simulation program. Other factors which may bear importantly on flood damages are flow velocity and duration of flooding; secondary phenomena, for example, sedimentation and scour, are functionally related to the major factors: stage, velocity, and duration.

Establishing stage-discharge functions is a straightforward exercise in hydrologic measurement for which well-developed techniques are available, although it is recognized that changing channel characteristics might require varying stage-discharge functions over the time of analysis. Creation of damage-stage functions, on the other hand, is a more complex problem involving many assumptions concerning human behavior under the threat of floods and of the economic impact of floods on the entire community. Standard practice is to classify flood losses as tangible or intangible. Tangible flood losses are taken as (i) the value of structures, facilities, and contents destroyed or damaged (computed as the cost of replacement or restoration to pre-flood status), and (ii) increases in cost of producing the goods and services associated with the damaged facilities. Intangible losses are those associated with loss of life, occurrence of disease, and deterioration of general welfare caused by flooding.[48]

Applying these concepts and techniques to estimation of losses from an historical flood is a direct although detailed and tedious exercise. The method in common use relies primarily on the interview technique, in which those suffering flood losses are asked to estimate the magnitude of damage. Even under this method, however, some use is made of standard relationships of losses to depth of inundation for typical residential structures. An alternative method, proposed by White and further developed by Kates, but not yet applied in actual system design, relies almost entirely on such standard relationships of loss to depth of inundation for residential, commercial, and industrial structures.[49] This technique promises to improve the quality of damage estimates by replacing much of the subjective judgment inherent in an interview with objective measurement of loss to structures and contents based on the extent of flooding.

[48] For details on estimating flood losses, see Eckstein, reference 45, pp. 127–144.
[49] White and Kates, reference 28.

Estimates of actual flood losses are used primarily as data for computing points on the damage–discharge function. These data must be adjusted to account for changes in patterns of land use and for man's reaction to flood warnings. These adjustments can affect estimates of future losses in either direction.

An assumption often made is that economic development of the flood plain will increase when flood protection is provided; hence, future flood losses for a given flood stage would necessarily exceed historic losses. But other assumptions must also be considered: (1) that some areas subject to serious flood hazard might be converted to uses more compatible with occasional flooding— parks, open spaces, parking lots; (2) that buildings can be flood-proofed; (3) that future development be prohibited in areas of severe flood hazard; and (4) that flood warning systems, combined with advance plans for moving stock and equipment to higher ground, can be instituted. Implementation of these practices would reduce flood losses below levels experienced in historic floods, economic development remaining fixed.[50]

Conceptually, there is a unique damage-discharge function associated with each assumption or combination of assumptions as to flood-plain occupancy and use. Several such functions, reflecting alternative degrees of flood-plain management, could well be constructed for use in simulation analysis. Figure 2.29 shows two such functions for urban land use, one assuming no management program, the other assuming a program of flood-proofing, zoning, and flood-warning. Agricultural losses are related also to the growing season, so that their numeric value is related to a family of functions rather than a single function which is insensitive to season.

For the Lehigh simulation we find it desirable to combine detailed data on 20 flood-damage zones, available from the Corps of Engineers Delaware basin study, into five damage–discharge functions as follows:

Allentown–Bethlehem	(14 zones)
Walnutport	(3 zones)
Aquashicola Creek	(1 zone)
Jordan Creek	(1 zone)
Pohopoco Creek	(1 zone)

[50] For detailed discussion of such alternative adjustments to flood hazard, see White and Kates, reference 28.

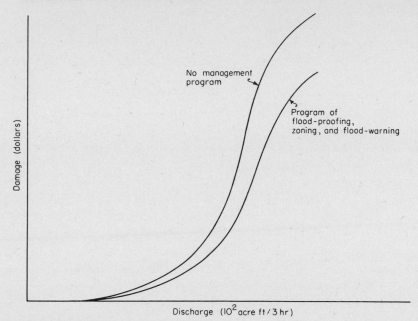

FIG. 2.29. Flood damage–discharge functions based on alternative management assumptions.

These functions are shown in Figs. 2.30, 2.31 and 2.32. The sharp change in slope of the Allentown–Bethlehem curve above 215×10^2 acre ft represents damages associated with overtopping an existing levee in Bethlehem which protects a high-value industrial area. It should be recalled that reservoir storage is the only design variable which affects flood-control benefits in this study. Local protection measures, such as levees and channel improvements, are not included because no detailed data on them were available in the Corps of Engineers Delaware basin study.

The damage–discharge functions for the Lehigh are based on the 1959 level of economic development with no allowance for future economic growth or for measures for flood plain management. These factors are taken into account in the simulation program, however, by applying an adjustment factor (which is an input variable) to increase or decrease damages by a constant proportion over the entire damage–discharge function. For example, assuming economic growth but no flood-plain management, the adjustment for the Lehigh system is contained in a growth factor of 0.004 per year, which was used for the Lehigh by the Corps of Engineers in the Delaware basin study.

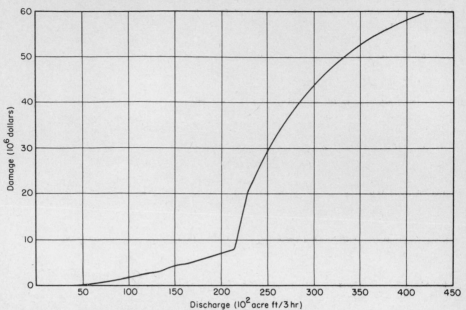

FIG. 2.30. Flood damage–discharge function, Bethlehem–Allentown zones, Lehigh River system.

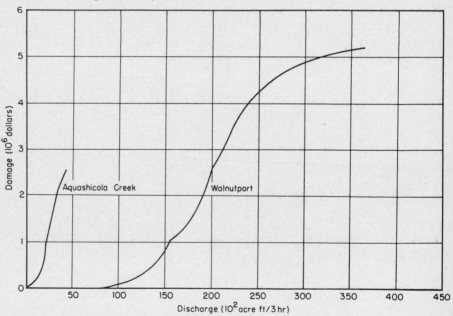

FIG. 2.31. Flood damage–discharge functions, Aquashicola Creek and Walnutport zones, Lehigh River system.

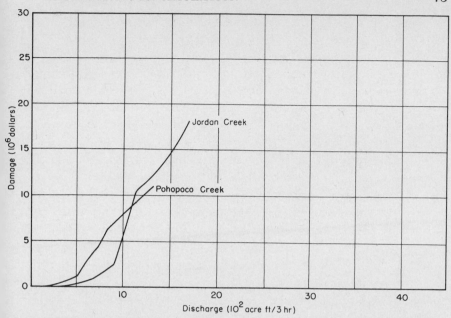

FIG. 2.32. Flood damage–discharge functions, Jordan Creek and Pohopoco Creek zones, Lehigh River system.

Benefit functions for water quality. The water-quality problem in most basins involves a number of pollution sources and is characterized by hydrologic uncertainty and temporal and spatial fluctuations; its indices include a plethora of related quality measurements, as for example, biochemical oxygen demand, hardness, alkalinity, turbidity, dissolved solids, radioactivity flux, dissolved oxygen, temperature, iron, and phenol. Thus, while water-quality improvement in a multipurpose system may be thought of simply as productive of a stream whose output is cleaner than its input, the technologic and economic relationships needed to deal effectively with water quality in simulation are difficult to attain.[51] In fact, water quality and quantity are often so highly correlated that it is difficult to treat benefit functions for water quality independently from those for water supply. For example, irrigation water must meet rigid quality requirements so that quantity without assured quality is meaningless; at the opposite extreme, an estuary poses problems of quality without significant opportunity for

[51] G. M. Fair and J. C. Geyer, *Water supply and waste-water disposal* (John Wiley, New York, 1956); A. V. Kneese, reference 41.

management of quantity. In this last case it is desirable to deal explicitly with the water-quality benefit function.

For simulation analysis we wish to devise functions relating water-quality benefits to assured minimum flows at critical points or zones on the stream. Such functions must be derived by combining a technologic function which relates stream quality to volume of flow and an economic function which relates benefits to improvements in stream quality.

The quality index, itself a scalar, typically involves a vector of pollutants, and the relationship between the index and flow rate incorporates many factors. Statistical techniques (for example, multivariate analysis) can be used as the basis of a procedure for estimating quality as a function of flow rate. Low flows are statistically related to high temperatures, which in turn occur simultaneously with high pollution levels. Thus a meaningful statistical relation between flow rate (independent variable) and quality (dependent variable) can be educed, yielding a distribution of the quality index for any flow rate.

The economic function relating benefits to improvement in quality is exactly analogous to the benefit function for water supply described on page 59, and its derivation involves problems similar in concept and measurement (see Figs. 2.23 and 2.24 above and related discussion). The benefits from achieving a given level of water quality by flow augmentation are measured by the lesser of (1) the willingness to pay of those adversely affected by the pollution, or (2) the cost of external alternatives (in this case, treatment of wastes before entry to the stream or treatment of the water at the point of use).[52]

In preparing the Lehigh simulation, we find no data on the technological function relating water quality to flow rate. However, the Lehigh simulation program is so written that we can establish a minimum flow constraint at Bethlehem for water-quality improvement, and by so doing determine the costs (in terms of benefits foregone) of meeting these constraints. Thus, if quality–quantity relationships become available, it would be possible to assess the

---

[52] As Kneese (reference 41) points out, the system can be defined so as to include waste treatment and water supply treatment measures as internal alternatives; under such circumstances, it is necessary to make estimates of willingness-to-pay of actual and potential users who would be adversely affected.

implications on quality of any mode of operation in the Lehigh system. In the absence of technological data, we offer no attempt to construct a benefit–quality function for the Lehigh.

Benefit functions for other purposes. Construction of benefit functions for other purposes, such as navigation and fish and wildlife enhancement, is similar in concept and method to those discussed above. For example, open channel navigation, as on the Missouri River, is directly related to controlling channel depth which is a function of flow rate. The alternative cost method of measuring benefits as described for water supply above, is applicable to cases where demand for the transportation can be reliably estimated. As for water supply, where demand cannot be assumed, estimates must be made of willingness to pay. Fish and wildlife benefit functions are analogous to benefit functions for recreation (at least for those fish and wildlife values where consumer demand is the important factor), and the same concepts and techniques of measurement are applicable as for recreation.

Economic-Loss Functions

For those system outputs to which targets are assigned — water supply, electric power, recreation, irrigation, and water-quality improvement — short-run economic-loss functions of the form shown in Fig. 2.22 must be constructed. These functions are used to evaluate the economic consequences of failures to meet target outputs. The magnitudes of these economic losses can be compared with costs involved in establishing lower targets or providing larger structures.[53]

Water supply. To construct short-range loss functions for water supply we must analyze water-user operations, including the adjustments which industry and municipal water systems make when faced with water-supply deficit. In industrial processes for which water is a vital ingredient, standby supplies are usually provided as a matter of course. The incremental cost of bringing these supplies into service may be said to measure the loss associated with the water deficit. Some industries may not maintain standby supplies, and may be able to sustain some shortage by altered operations — all at a cost. To some users, severe losses may mean

---

[53] The concept of the economic-loss function and its application to a specific case are described in Maass, Hufschmidt, *et al.*, reference 10, pp. 156, 274.

total plant shutdown and heavy (if not intolerable) costs. Similarly, muncipalities may ameliorate shortages by maintaining standby supplies, or by restricting water use, at varying costs.

Recognizing a functional relationship between deficits and the costs occasioned by them, we have constructed for the Lehigh the curves shown in Fig. 2.33. The composition of Lehigh water-supply demand is industrial (80 percent) and municipal (20 percent). Because the data are incomplete, both the magnitude of economic loss per unit deficit and the rate of increase in economic loss as the deficit increases are only rough estimates. They do illustrate the concept, however, and emphasize the need for additional research. It will be observed that a prohibitive loss is imposed at the 50 percent deficit level. This serves to reject as obviously nonoptimal any system designs with deficits at or above the 50 percent level and restricts the search to designs which can be expected to produce smaller deficits.

Power. The loss associated with energy deficits may be measured by costs incurred by the power system in turning to the next cheap-

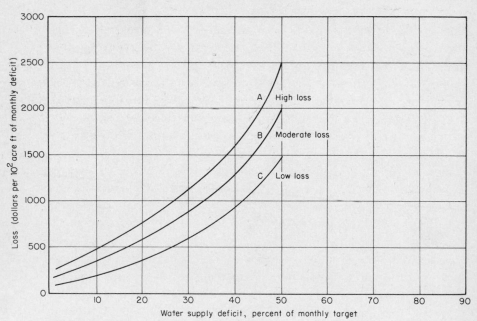

FIG. 2.33. Unit water-supply loss functions, Lehigh River system, under various assumptions of severity of loss. Losses over 50 percent of monthly target are valued at 10^5 dollars per 10^2 acre ft.

est source of equivalent power generation. This source will vary at any given time from cheap energy interchanges to costly start-up of old standby thermal capacity. Deficits are, in effect, unscheduled shortages which could occur when all efficient sources of system production are fully committed.

In cases where shortages are severe or frequent, power from the system can no longer be termed "firm" or "dependable peaking" within the terms of a contractual obligation. As purchasers normally insist on 100 percent availability under a pricing structure for firm power, severe shortages in supply must necessarily bear a heavy penalty.

The loss function constructed for the Lehigh simulation has the following characteristics: (a) losses per kilowatt-hour of deficit are estimated at 1.5 cents for the full range of assumed load factors; (b) in the event that monthly deficits exceed 25 percent of the target output for the month, a heavy penalty of 10^3 dollars per kilowatt-hour of deficit is imposed (see Fig. 2.34).

Recreation. The recreation value of a reservoir site is impaired by wide fluctuations in reservoir level. From the standpoint of recreation alone it is desirable to maintain reservoir pools of substantially constant levels, especially during periods of heavy recreational use. Where other purposes are to be served, it may be necessary to draw down the reservoirs even during the prime rec-

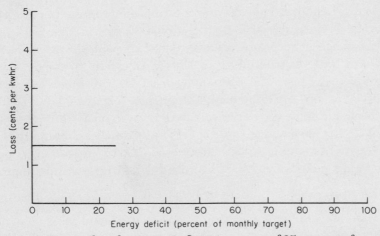

FIG. 2.34. Energy-loss function. Deficits in excess of 25 percent of monthly target are penalized at 10^3 dollar per kwhr.

reation season. We wish, therefore, to construct functions which relate short-term recreation losses to the extent of reservoir drawdown.

In practice it is convenient, first, to relate losses in visitor-days of recreation attendance, computed from some base or long-run attendance level, to magnitude of drawdown from a target recreation pool level, and then to multiply visitor-day losses by a monetary value per visitor-day to obtain an economic-loss function. This is not equivalent to a linear loss function, because nonlinearity is implicit in the relationship between reservoir contents and visitor-days of attendance.

The exact dependence of losses in recreation attendance on drawdown is unique for each reservoir. While climate, availability of alternative sites, and type of recreation development may be significant factors, the overriding influence is shoreline topography. For sites with shallow slopes, even a small reduction in reservoir level exposes a large area of reservoir bed, adversely affecting recreational use; conversely, for relatively steep slopes, the rate of exposure is slow, and recreational uses might be little affected.

There are few data on the response of recreation attendance to drawdown at existing reservoirs in the United States. But we can expect, as both numbers of public reservoirs and intensity of their use expand, that much information will be made available for use in constructing loss functions.[54]

For the Lehigh area, we propose a single set of loss functions for all six reservoir sites. This set of curves, shown in Fig. 2.35, presents a range of responses of attendance to pool elevation, based upon the limited available data. The justification for these curves is: drawdowns less than 15 feet from target pool levels cause no appreciable loss in attendance;[55] those in excess of 60, 80, or 100 feet (depending on the curve selected) impose no additional losses beyond those incurred at these levels because we assume that only 80 percent of attendance is related to pool level—the other 20 percent being picnickers, hikers, and others using the surrounding

[54] Some information is contained in the following references: U. S. Tennessee Valley Authority, *Outdoor recreation for a growing nation—TVA's experience with man-made reservoirs* (1961) Appendix C, and U. S. Geological Survey, *Water for recreation, values and opportunities,* report to the Outdoor Recreation Resources Review Commission (ORRRC Study report no. 10, Washington, 1962).

[55] See *Delaware River basin,* reference 1, vol. I, p. 138.

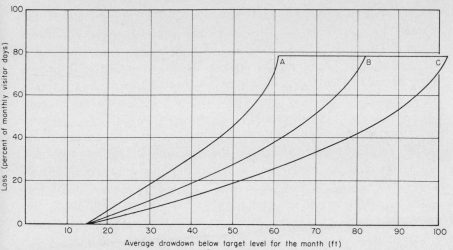

FIG. 2.35. Recreation loss functions, Lehigh River system, under various assumptions of severity of loss.

lands as distinct from boaters and swimmers using the waters; the rate of attendance loss between these drawdown levels increases with increased drawdown.

Economic losses are related ultimately to the drawdown and its temporal extent. The Lehigh simulation program computes initial and final monthly storage and interpolates linearly between them to determine the fraction of time that storage falls below the recreation constraint. The drawdown curve and the visitor-day loss curves are converted into an economic loss by evaluating the definite integral of their product, the limits of integration being those two times between which the constraint is violated.

Irrigation. In concept, the irrigation-loss function is similar to that for water supply and power. Detailed effects of deficits are functions of time of occurrences, degree of advance knowledge, and flexibility of the production process. In some cases, the effects of severe deficits may extend into subsequent seasons, as in orchard damage.

There are substantial data on response of irrigated crops to deficits; construction of irrigation-loss functions can therefore proceed with some assurance, although there is a unique function for each assumed pattern of irrigation use. An example is shown in Fig. 2.27, curve B.[56]

[56] For further details, see Maass, Hufschmidt, *et al.*, reference 10, pp. 275–278.

Water-quality improvement. Economic-loss functions for water quality are identical in concept to the loss functions for water supply. Given a target level of water quality, the consequences of failures to achieve the target are assessed by estimating short-run losses to industries, municipalities, recreation, and fisheries, either in terms of the value of lost production or resources or of the cost of emergency measures needed to counteract the effects of degraded stream quality. With the current recognition of the importance of water-quality management, extensive data collection programs are being initiated; research into systems analysis of data collection networks will form the basis for construction of economic-loss functions for quality.[57]

Floos-damage prevention. No special loss function need be derived for flood-damage prevention, because the damage–discharge functions discussed above are a special form of loss function. In effect, we evaluate flood prevention benefits by subtracting flood losses which would occur under the proposed design from those which would be suffered under the existing system.

ARRANGING FOR SUMMARY ECONOMIC ANALYSES

There are many ways to examine the performance of a simulated system; for example, one could focus attention on detailed behavior of the system—the month-by-month trace of the outputs and state of the system, including contents in storage reservoirs, river stages, and volumes of water supply and energy provided.[58] For long simulations of water-resource systems, information in this much detail would be too voluminous to be useful; information of a summary nature is far more appropriate. Furthermore, we are primarily interested in the economic consequences of the performance of a particular design, although we also find that data on physical performance are useful in their own right.

In the previous section we describe how cost-input and benefit-output functions can be prepared in forms useful in simulation

---

[57] Kneese, reference 41, and R. V. Thomann and M. J. Sobel, "Estuarine water quality management and forecasting," *Proc. Am. Soc. Civil Engrs.*, 90 SA 5 (October 1964).

[58] Indeed, in certain business simulations, these traces of experience over time, including behavior of inventories, level of working capital, and the like, are the relevant outputs for analysis of system performance. See J. W. Forrester, *Industrial dynamics* (M.I.T. Press and John Wiley, New York, 1961), chap. 2.

analysis. Here we describe how these functions can be used to derive the economic consequences of a particular design.

In general, we define the economic consequences of a system in terms of the present value of the stream of benefits less capital and OMR costs over the economic life of the project. Capital costs are assumed to be incurred either entirely at the outset, or, alternatively, at only a few points in time over the period of economic analysis. On the other hand, benefits and OMR costs are assumed to occur as *annual* values over the period of economic analysis.

It is possible to arrange a simulation program so as to translate physical performance into economic consequences in a number of different ways, including the following categories:

1. Types of investment programs
   (a) Static—single-period investments
   (b) Dynamic—investments spread over time

2. Methods of discounting benefit streams
   (a) Annual benefits discounted to the present from year of occurrence
   (b) Annual benefits summed and averaged, and the stream of equal annual benefits discounted to the present

3. Length of simulation periods
   (a) Simulation period equal to the length of the period of economic analysis
   (b) Simulation period greater than the period of economic analysis

These categories constitute a matrix from which eight types of simulation runs can be established. Of these, we find that the following four types are of primary interest:

I. Static analysis
   A. Benefits are discounted from the year of occurrence, and the simulation period equals the period of economic analysis.
   B. Benefits are discounted after being converted to a stream of equal annual values, and the simulation period exceeds the period of economic analysis.

II. Dynamic analysis
  A. Benefits are discounted from the year of occurrence, and the simulation period equals the period of economic analysis.
  B. Benefits are discounted after being converted to a stream of equal annual values, and the simulation period exceeds the period of economic analysis.

The major characteristics of these types of analyses are presented in the following sections.

I. Static Analysis

For these analyses, whether sub-types A or B, the simulation program is arranged so that (i) all capital facilities are assumed to be installed at the beginning of the first year of the period of economic analysis, and (ii) target outputs for all purposes remain fixed over the entire period of economic analysis. Capital costs thus require no discounting; OMR costs, which occur as a stream of equal annual values, and annual values of benefits, are discounted to year one using a discount rate or set of rates which are preset program parameters. Total discounted benefits less discounted OMR costs and undiscounted capital costs yields the desired payoff — present value of net system benefits.

A. *Benefits discounted from year of occurrence.* A simulation run yields, for each year of the period of economic analysis, physical performance and associated benefits for each purpose. The sequence of annual benefits is discounted to year one by applying to the benefits for each year the discount operator $1/(1 + i)^n$ where i is the specified discount rate and n is the year of occurrence in question. For positive values of the discount rate, the present value of the benefits for any particular year thus depends on its position in the period of economic analysis, later years having lower present values for identical benefits than earlier years.

In contrast, OMR costs are treated as an equal annual stream and are discounted to the present by applying the discount operator $[(1 + i)^N - 1]/[i(1 + i)^N]$, where, again, i is the discount rate and N represents the length in years of the period of economic analysis.

Capital costs, which are undiscounted in this case, and the present value of OMR costs are deducted from the sum of present values of benefits to obtain a single payoff of present value of net benefits.

Where benefits are discounted from the year of occurrence it makes no sense to run simulations beyond the last year of the period of economic analysis. For this reason, both in this type (I.A) and in its dynamic counterpart (II.A), the practice of discounting benefits from the year of occurrence is associated with a simulation period equal to the period of economic analysis.

B. *Benefits discounted as streams of equal annual values.* In this type of analysis, annual benefits and their squares for each purpose are cumulated over the entire simulation period, and the mean and standard deviation of annual values are computed therefrom. These moments, not the individual annual values, are discounted to the present. OMR and capital costs are handled as in section A, above.

The fact that we compute means and standard deviations of benefits before discounting frees us from the requirement that the period of simulation be limited in length to the period of economic analysis. While we can so limit the simulation period if we choose, it is preferable to run simulations for much longer periods in order to test performance of the system subject to many sequences of high and low flows. The mean and standard deviation of gross system benefits are thus independent of a single historical trace of hydrology.

Both in this type of analysis (I.B) and in its dynamic counterpart (II.B) the practice of discounting benefits as streams of equal annual values is associated with a simulation period which is longer than the period of economic analysis.

II. Dynamic analysis

For these analyses, we drop the assumption that all capital facilities are installed at the start of year one and that the levels of target outputs remain unchanged throughout the period of economic analysis. Instead, capital inputs and levels of target outputs are allowed to change singly or jointly at selected times throughout the period of economic analysis. The period during which capital inputs and target outputs remain fixed is defined as a *demand period.* By using multiple demand periods it is possible to examine the physical performance and economic consequences of a dynamic system; that is, we analyze alternative schedules of investment and output levels in terms both of physical performance and of payoffs in present value of net benefits.

A. *Benefits discounted from year of occurrence.* Analysis of economic consequences of this case proceeds as its counterpart in static analysis (I.A) with two exceptions. (1) Capital investments, which can now occur in later years of the period of economic analysis, are discounted to the present. The discount operator $1/(1+i)^n$ is used for this purpose. (2) OMR costs can no longer be treated as a stream of equal annual values over the entire period of economic analysis, because, in general, they have a different value for each demand period. Rather, OMR costs are identified by year of occurrence, and the discount operator $1/(1+i)^n$ is applied to the values for each year so that the results can be summed to obtain present value of OMR costs.

The streams of annual benefits will continue to be discounted as before, with the discount operator $1/(1+i)^n$ applied to benefit values for each year.

This case—dynamic analysis with benefits discounted from year of occurrence—differs from its static counterpart only in the timing of capital outlays and changes in the levels of target outputs and OMR costs during the period of economic analysis. In both cases the simulation period is coterminous with the period of economic analysis. Both examine the performance of the system with only a single trace of the hydrology, and in both cases the present values of gross and net benefits are influenced by the particular configuration of hydrology that is used.

One way of compensating for this dependence of payoff on a particular hydrologic trace is to run several simulations of the system design, using different traces of hydrology (these being provided by the operational hydrology generator described on pages 15–24), and to observe the distribution of payoffs from the individual runs and, perhaps, compute the average payoff.[59]

B. *Benefits discounted as streams of equal annual values.* Analysis here is analogous to its static counterpart except that the annual averages and standard deviations of benefits are computed for each

[59] This method was used in the simulation analysis reported in Maass, Hufschmidt, *et al.*, reference 10, pp. 486–493.

demand period. The streams of average annual benefits and their standard deviations for each demand period are then discounted to year one, taking account of the position of the demand periods in relation to the period of economic analysis. As shown in Fig. 2.36, for a design with a 90-year period of economic analysis and three demand periods of 15, 25, and 50 years' duration, respectively, the discount operator $[(1+)^n - 1]/[i(1+i)^n]$ is applied to the first demand period, with $n = 15$; for the second and third demand periods, the streams of equal annual benefits from year 16 to year 40, and from year 41 to year 90, respectively, are discounted to year one. The sum of discounted benefits for the three demand periods yields the present value of total gross benefits for the entire period of economic analysis.

Capital and OMR costs are discounted to year one as in the dynamic case described in the preceding section, and the payoff in present value of net benefits is computed as before. As in the static counterpart, length of the simulation period generally exceeds the period of economic analysis.

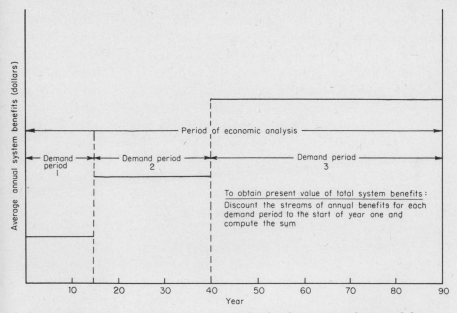

FIG. 2.36. Time profile of system benefits for dynamic analysis with benefits discounted as stream of equal annual values.

Summary

We have shown that water-resource system simulations can be constructed to (1) take advantage of operational hydrology by simulating for any desired period, and (2) treat dynamic investment programs through the device of dividing the period of economic analysis into demand periods within which capital investment and levels of target outputs are fixed. Simulation periods (length of simulation runs) need not and in general should not be identical to demand periods.

The Lehigh simulation program, to be described in detail in Chapter 3, can handle all types of simulation runs described above. It is thus possible to analyze the economic performance of a selected water-resource system in the way best suited to the nature of the system and to the physical and economic data available.

3 THE LEHIGH SIMULATION PROGRAM

The Lehigh River system simulation program, described in the following pages, illustrates the application of simulation to a water-resource system of moderate size and complexity.

In fact, the computer program for the Lehigh simulation represents an enormous coding effort. It consists of a main routine and twenty-two subroutines, and the compiled or binary object program occupies 32,744 memory locations, leaving a scant 24 registers of the IBM 7094 computer unused. There are numerous coding inefficiencies in the current version of the Lehigh program. A second writing could replace many of these by more direct and streamlined constructions. Even the most efficient program, however, would be of formidable size.

Before discussing the individual routines in detail it is necessary to define several terms which will be used throughout the discussion. These terms are related to each other hierarchically in that they describe successively smaller segments of the simulation program. The *job* constitutes a submission of the entire program and associated input data to the computer. Every time the program and data decks are deposited at the computing installation, another job is initiated. Each job includes certain *invariants,* or data, seldom changed, which describe economic, structural, and physical relationships at the several sites and points or zones of water use. For example, the head-contents curves and capital cost curves at all reservoir sites are considered invariant data, to be changed only if a potential site is moved or if the preliminary economic analysis must be modified.

Each job consists, in turn, of one or more *studies.* Each study investigates a particular combination of design *variables* and schedules of development. In turn, each study may be subdivided into several *runs,* each dealing with a *demand period* or portion of the economic time horizon associated with the problem. Depending upon the purpose of the study and the method of discounting incorporated in the benefit evaluation procedure, the length of simulation may or may not be identical to the length of each demand period.

Finally, within each run, the program executes several *algorithms.* An algorithm is an iterative sequence of computations which re-uses previously computed intermediate results to refine or converge upon the solution. The Lehigh simulation program utilizes 7 algorithms; each of the short algorithms is contained in a single subroutine, whereas each of the long algorithms requires several constituent subroutines in tandem. Some programmers refer to these long algorithms as *packages*, reserving the term *algorithm* for smaller units of the computation.

Figure 3.1 shows the flow of control in the simulation program. The invariants are read at the start of each job, and it is clear that to investigate a new configuration of dam sites it is necessary to restart the entire computation. In the next step the run is initialized, and the data uniquely associated with that run are read from magnetic tape. Three classes of input data are required for a run: (i) hydrologic parameters for generating monthly and flood flows; (ii) system-design variables; (iii) run-control variables. The hydrologic variables of (i) are the moments, correlation coefficients, regression coefficients, and flood parameters previously extracted from the monthly and flood records by analysis of the historical flows. If the run is to use historical instead of synthetic hydrologic data, the moments of the synthetic hydrology generators are bypassed in favor of the necessary historical monthly and flood flows. The system-design variables required in group (ii) comprise the sizes and capacities of structures, power and water supply targets, constraints on flood and recreation storage levels, and other values listed in Tables 2.3 and 2.5. The control variables, group (iii), give the length of simulation analysis, beginning and end of demand periods, and values which define the design Case and mode of discounting.

The hydrologic data are provided on a permanent magnetic tape which is repositioned for each run. The system-design variables require 67 cards, and a complete packet must be provided for each

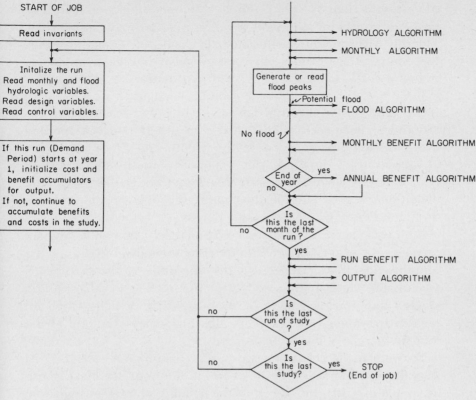

FIG. 3.1. General flow chart of the Lehigh simulation program.

run. The control variables are punched on four cards so that the input deck for each run consists of 71 cards.

The program investigates whether a new study is to be undertaken by examining the start of the demand period. If the run (or demand period) starts in year 1, a new study is presumed to begin, and the cost and benefit accumulators are cleared for the study. If the run begins in a year other than 1, it is presumed to be part of a continuing study and the costs and benefits are allowed to accumulate in their respective registers.

Having dispensed with the preliminaries, the program enters the main loop which is traversed once for each month of the simulation period. The Hydrology Algorithm is called first, and monthly flows, whether generated here (for a synthetic run) or read (for a historical run), are made available to the main routine. The Monthly

Algorithm is then executed; releases are made to meet, insofar as possible, targets for minimum flows, power and water supply. The Monthly Algorithm is a composite of five subroutines, and performs the computations which characterize what hydraulic engineers ordinarily call the monthly operation procedure.

If the run utilizes synthetic hydrology, flood peaks are generated; if the run utilizes historical flows, the record is examined to determine if a flood occurs in the current month. If there is a recorded or potential synthetic flood in the month, the Flood Algorithm (4 subroutines) is invoked. This group of subroutines generates or reads 3-hourly flood flows and routes them through the system; the conditional branch point leading to the Flood Algorithm is shown on Fig. 3.1.

After considering monthly and, possibly, flood flows, the program proceeds to evaluation of the monthly benefits by calling the Monthly Benefit Algorithm, a single subroutine. At the end of each year of the simulation period, the Annual Benefit Algorithm, a single subroutine, is called to accumulate those benefits which are recorded as annual values. This algorithm marks the end of the loop on months of the simulation period.

To evaluate the entire demand period, the program calls the Run Benefit Algorithm, a composite of two subroutines; the first of these accumulates, edits, and discounts the benefits for final presentation, and the second evaluates the capital and OMR costs associated with the several components of the system and, where appropriate, accumulates, edits, and discounts these values. Finally, the Output Algorithm is called to tabulate the several costs and benefits, compute the net benefits, and provide summaries of (i) the initial inputs, (ii) the physical performance of the system, and (iii) the economic performance of the system.

Having completed a run, the program inquires whether another run (characterized by an additional 71 cards) is to be processed, either to further the current study or to initiate a new study. If so, the program is restarted as shown in Fig. 3.1, but the invariant data are not read again. If no further runs are to be made, the study and job are completed and the program is terminated. As a general guide, a 50-year simulation run of the Lehigh Program requires 1.5 minutes of machine time. This time is increased slightly if there are several short demand periods because the Run Benefit Algorithm and Output Algorithm are called at the end of each demand period. However, compared to the generation and routing of flows through the system, these summary algorithms require little time and their execution time can be disregarded in estimating the length of a job.

The following sections discuss the seven algorithms and related routines in detail; of these seven, the Monthly Algorithm is supported by detailed flow charts presented in a condensed format devised especially for this book. A key to the symbols used in the charts is contained in Appendix I. The Flood Algorithm is supported by a hydrograph while the remaining computations are explained by their algebraic equivalents or descriptive text. A glossary of FORTRAN mnemonics is included in Appendix II.

THE EXECUTIVE ROUTINES

Five routines are required to start the program and initialize all relevant registers. These routines consist of the MAIN program and four satellite routines (READ1, READ2, SETUP, and SETUPB).

In the earlier discussion of the operational hydrology generator in Chapter 2 it is noted, at least for the IBM 7094 System used in this study, that the program regenerates synthetic traces of monthly and flood flows for each run because (i) it is faster to recompute these values than to read them from tape, and (ii) generating these values each month provides great flexibility in testing the response of the system by allowing any combination of design variables to be tested with many different configurations of hydrology. At the same time, of course, any pattern of hydrologic input can be reproduced by setting the random number generator at an appropriate starting point. The MAIN program and the four subroutines read and store the data upon which the hydrology generating model is predicated, and initialize the registers in which the benefits and various counters are accumulated.

MAIN program

(1) The MAIN Program calls Subroutine READ1, which reads the design variables and control data from the system input tape. Subroutine READ2 is then called, and under its control the parameters for generating operational monthly and flood hydrology are read into core from auxiliary tape storage.

(2) Subroutine SETUPB is called to initialize the registers in which benefits are accumulated and to compute the nominal benefits which accrue to the several target levels of output.

(3) Subroutine SETUP is called to calculate the coefficients of the linear transforms required by the operational hydrology generating model.

(4) A loop on months is established, its limits being month 1 and the end of the simulation period. Within the range of the loop the following algorithms are called:

    (i) Hydrology Algorithm,

    (ii) Monthly Algorithm,

    (iii) Flood Algorithm, and

    (iv) Monthly Benefit Algorithm.

At the end of each year of the simulation, the Annual Benefit Algorithm is called, and finally, when the loop is satisfied, the Run Benefit Algorithm and the Output Algorithm are called to summarize the run.

(5) The MAIN Program inquires whether another run and study is to be made, whereupon the program returns control to step (1) of the MAIN Program or terminates.

Subroutine SETUP

(1) Based on the correlation coefficients which obtain between all relevant pairs of stations, and on the first three moments of the distributions of historical flows, Subroutine SETUP computes the coefficients required by the operational hydrology generator. The output produced by this subroutine consists of the serial correlation coefficients for the several principal components and the regression coefficients whereby the flows at all sites are reconstituted from the serially extended components.

(2) Subroutine SETUP initializes the registers in which the flows and their first four powers and cross-products are accumulated. To verify the reliability of the operational hydrology, these powers and cross-products are accumulated in Subroutine SYNHYD so that the moments of the flow distributions can be computed at the end of each run. Any marked deviation of these computed moments from the assumed population values, reflected by the inputs, indicates that the model does not faithfully reproduce the flows in all pertinent details.

Subroutine SETUPB

(1) The program initializes those registers in which the monthly and annual benefits are accumulated and in which the various measures of system performance are tabulated.

(2) The program evaluates the nominal benefits from water supply and power, using a series of cubic equations fitted by a spline technique to a sequence of numeric data; in each case the benefits are functions of the annual targets. For recreation, the nominal benefit is computed as a double sum of the benefits accruing (i) in each month, and (ii) at each site. Owing to the seasonal distribution of demand for recreation, and to the differing adaptability of each site to recreational use, this cumbersome summation procedure is required.

Subroutine READ1

(1) The design variables and simulation control data are read from the system input tape for each run.

(2) Conversion from reservoir height to reservoir storage is performed; the input parameters which characterize the reservoir recreation levels (see the Monthly Algorithm below) are reservoir surface elevations and these are converted to reservoir storage values using the spline technique mentioned in Subroutine SETUPB above.

Subroutine READ2

(1) The program inquires whether the hydrology generators, both monthly and flood, are to utilize logarithmic transforms. The appropriate moments of historical flows, appropriately transformed or not, are read from auxiliary tape storage.

(2) If the run is to use historical data, the recorded monthly and flood flows are read from auxiliary tape and stored for subsequent use during the simulation.

No computations are undertaken by this subroutine.

THE HYDROLOGY ALGORITHM

Much of the theoretical justification for the generation of operational hydrology appears elsewhere in this book. Although based on substantial statistical manipulation, the results of the model for generating monthly operational hydrology are disarmingly simple;

consequently, the entire computation is contained in a single sub-routine, Subroutine SYNHYD, whose operation consists of evaluating a linear transformation.

Subroutine SYNHYD

(1) The hydrology generator tests to determine which of four possible alternatives is requested:

  (i) normally distributed flows,
  (ii) log-normally distributed flows,
  (iii) gamma-distributed flows, or
  (iv) historical flows.

For all cases except (iv), the program first computes the current value of eight principal components. Each component is a linear combination, or blend of flows, at the following sites: Tobyhanna, Bear Creek, Mahoning, Beltzville, Aquashicola, Trexler, Tannery, and Bethlehem. Walnutport, a central site in development of synthetic flood hydrographs, is not utilized in generating monthly hydrology.

(2) Using the coefficients computed in Subroutine SETUP, the program converts the eight principal component values into flows at the respective sites.

(3) The flows and their powers (up through the fourth) are accumulated for subsequent calculation of moments.

(4) For case (iv) above, the analysis using historical flows, the generation and accumulation of synthetic flows are overridden by selection of the appropriate historical flow from among those in storage.

(5) Whether the monthly data are generated or obtained from the recorded flows, the eight monthly flow values are delivered to the MAIN Routine for use in subsequent computation.

THE MONTHLY ALGORITHM IN DETAIL

A.   Basic Policy

The basic policy is, first, to provide for certain specified minimum stream flows below the reservoirs and, second, to meet the target outputs for (1) water supply at Bethlehem and (2) electric energy for the system, subject to specified constraints on minimum reservoir contents for recreation and on maximum reservoir contents for storage of flood waters.

Inflows that cannot be stored within the constrained reservoir range are used to generate electric energy, subject to the available capacity of penstocks and turbines, and are counted as releases contributing toward meeting the water-supply target at Bethlehem. Flows in the Lehigh at the point of diversion to Mahoning (reservoir 3) that are not needed to meet the water-supply target are diverted to reservoir 3, subject to the limitations of the diversion channel or available space in reservoir 3.

Releases required to meet the water-supply target are made first from reservoir 1 or 2, subject to a recreation constraint on minimum reservoir contents. If necessary, additional releases are made from reservoirs 3, 4, 5, and 6, according to a rule which apportions the releases so that the total remaining storage space is divided among the reservoirs in accordance with certain derived proportions. These proportions are designed to equalize the probability of spill among the four reservoirs over the remainder of the drawdown-refill cycle, given assumed patterns of future inflows.

If further releases are necessary to meet the water-supply target, reservoir 1 or 2 is again utilized with a revised recreation constraint which allows that reservoir to be drawn down below the initial constraint level. If further releases are required, they are made from reservoirs 3, 4, 5, and 6, according to the allocation rule described above, but with a revised (lower) constraint level on the contents of each reservoir.

All releases for water supply are routed through the hydroelectric plants subject to the limits of penstock and turbine capacities, but if these releases fail to generate sufficient energy to meet the target output, additional releases are made in the same four-part sequence as for water supply (i.e., reservoir 1 or 2; then 3, 4, 5, and 6; then 1 or 2 again; finally, 3, 4, 5, and 6).

If target outputs for water supply or energy are not met after releasing from all reservoirs to the full extent allowed by constraints on storage level and on penstock or turbine capacities, no further releases are made. Instead, the water-supply or energy deficits for the month are recorded. In any event, the Monthly Algorithm is terminated at this point, and control is returned to the MAIN Routine for investigation of floods and benefits.

B. The Subroutines in Detail

As shown in Fig. 3.2, the Monthly Algorithm consists of the following subroutines: BASIC, DIVERT, POWER, WATER, SUPPOW, and SPACE.

Subroutine BASIC handles the initial water bookkeeping, computing the inevitable flows that arise whenever the inflows plus initial contents exceed the normal or long-term storage capacities of the reservoirs, and computing as well the releases required to assure minimum flows below the several reservoirs;

Subroutine DIVERT handles diversions of water from the main stem of the Lehigh to reservoir 3;

Subroutine POWER computes the energy generated by all of the basic and supplementary releases from all reservoirs;

Subroutine WATER computes the supplementary releases required to meet the target output for water supply at Bethlehem;

Subroutine SUPPOW computes the supplementary releases required to meet the target output for energy; and

Subroutine SPACE allocates required releases among reservoirs 3, 4, 5, and 6.

The following sequences describe the several subroutines in detail; Figs. 3.3 to 3.8 provide further clarification. The calling se-

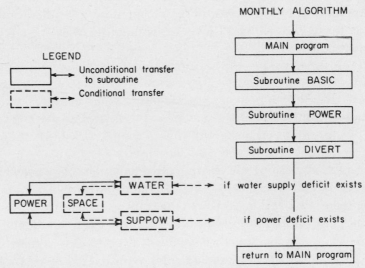

FIG. 3.2. Calling sequence of subroutines in the Monthly Algorithm.

quence appears in Fig. 3.2. The computation proceeds sequentially unless the special conditions indicated at the start of a step are encountered.

Subroutine BASIC (Fig. 3.3)

(1) For each reservoir, the basic release (+)[1] is defined as the sum of inflow and initial contents minus the allowable storage capacity (that is, the total storage capacity less the flood-storage allowance).

(2) For *Case 2:* the excess flow (+) is defined as the difference between the basic release and the minimum channel flow required below reservoir 1, this difference limited by the Beltzville penstock (or, more simply, the penstock) capacity. The computation is similar for *Cases* 4 and 5, except that the excess flow (+) is defined with respect to reservoir 2.

(3) For *Cases* 2 and 5, the basic release at reservoir 4 is redefined by adding to the previous value the newly defined excess flow. This has the effect of routing all of the water which is diverted from reservoir 1 (or 2) through reservoir 4, storing none; this is subsequently modified in Subroutine POWER.

(4) For each reservoir the shortage is defined as the difference between the minimum flow required at the reservoir and the basic release. If this shortage is not positive, the computation is completed for the reservoir, but if the shortage is positive, the first supplementary release, limited only by the water available in the reservoir, is made to meet the minimum flow requirement.

(5) The routine returns control to the MAIN Program, thence to Subroutine POWER.

Subroutine POWER (Fig. 3.4)

(1) The contents of all reservoirs are updated by computing the sum of the inflow and the initial contents, and subtracting from this the sum of the current basic and supplementary releases.

(2) For reservoir 3, the new (i.e., updated) contents are incremented by the diversion from the main stem. The first time that Subroutine POWER is called, the diversion is zero, so this computation does not change the contents. The additional supplementary release available for use at reservoir 3 is defined as the sum of the

---

[1] In this discussion, the symbol (+) will be taken to mean the stated quantity if this quantity be positive; otherwise, the quantity is modified so that its value is zero.

second and third supplementary releases made from reservoir 1 (or 2).[2]

(3) For reservoir 4, *Cases* 2 and 5, the computation defines the penstock flow as the sum of the excess flow and the second and third supplementary releases from reservoir 1 (or 2), this quantity limited by the penstock capacity. If no supplementary releases are required at this stage of the computation, zero is substituted for the relevant addends. In the event of a water-supply deficit at Bethlehem, the first supplementary release at reservoir 4 is incremented by the total flow through the penstock; that is, all the water arriving at the reservoir is routed directly through the turbines and thence downstream. Using these data, the basic release (+) and the updated contents at reservoir 4 are recomputed. The new contents are compared to the normal pool contents to ascertain that penstock

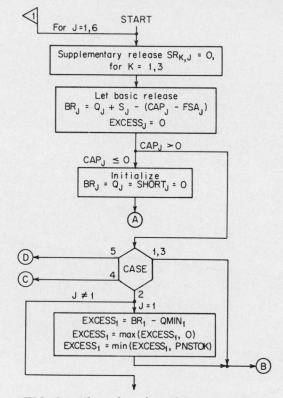

FIG. 3.3. Flow chart for subroutine BASIC.

[2] For *Case* 2 read reservoir 1 and for *Case* 5 read reservoir 2.

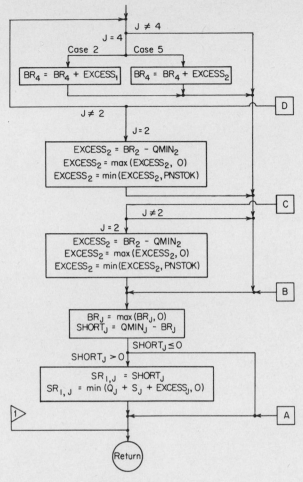

FIG. 3.3 (continued).

inflow does not raise the level to impinge on the space required for flood control; if so, additional supplementary releases are made. In the event that the penstock capacity limits the flow into reservoir 4, the unused water is routed directly downstream through the channel below reservoir 1 (or 2).

(4) Having updated all the reservoir content values, the program proceeds to evaluate the energy produced by the several releases at each reservoir. The average contents, being one half the sum of the initial contents and the current value of the contents, are computed. The total time, expressed as a fraction of a month

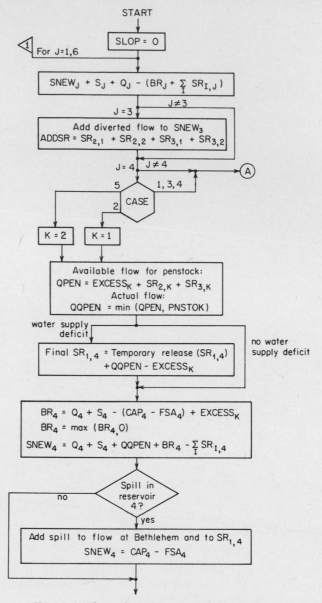

Fig. 3.4. Flow chart for subroutine POWER.

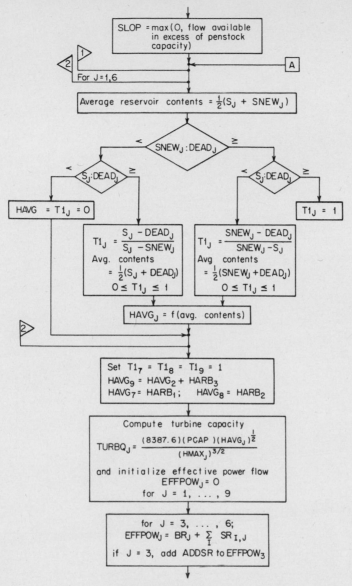

FIG. 3.4 (continued).

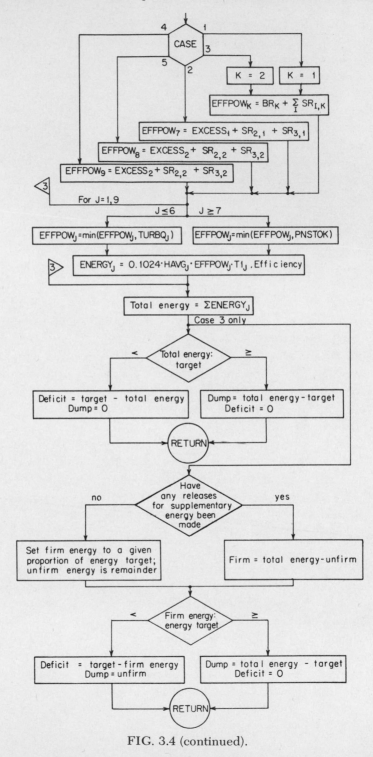

FIG. 3.4 (continued).

during which the contents are at or above the dead-storage level, is computed, utilizing the assumption that the reservoir contents change linearly during the course of the month.

(5) The average head at each of turbines 1 through 6 is evaluated by a polynomial function of reservoir contents. The average head at turbine 9 is computed by noting the fixed penstock drop (from the input data) and adding this to the appropriate reservoir head. The heads at turbines 7 and 8 are fixed by the penstock drop.

(6) The water capacity at each of the 9 turbines is evaluated as a function of average head and turbine characteristics (i.e., power capacity and maximum head).

(7) The effective power flow at turbines 4–6 is computed as the sum of the basic release and the three supplementary releases. The effective power flow at turbine 3 is computed in a similar fashion, except that the additional supplementary release (step 2) is included in the sum.

(8) For *Case 1*, the effective power flow at turbine 1 is computed as in step (7) above; the computation is similar for the effective power flow at turbine 2, *Case 3*.

(9) For *Case 2*, the effective power flow at turbine 7 is given by the sum of the excess flow and the second and third supplementary releases from reservoir 1; that is, it includes all the water released from reservoir 1 except that which is required to maintain minimum flow downstream of the site.

(10) For *Cases 4* and *5*, the effective power flow at turbine 9 (or 8) is given by the sum of the excess flow through the penstock and the second and third supplementary releases from reservoir 2.

(11) The effective power flows, however computed, are limited for all 9 turbines by the respective turbine water capacities.

(12) The energy produced at each of the 9 turbines is computed and accumulated, whereupon the total energy production is compared to the energy target, and a surplus or deficit is recorded.

(13) For *Case 3*, the total energy is divided into firm and unfirm portions; subsequent comparisons of energy production and target are based on the firm energy output only.

(14) If the target is met or exceeded, the energy deficit is set to zero and the dump energy is computed. If the target is not met, the dump energy is set to zero and the energy deficit is computed.

(15) Control is returned to the calling subroutine.

Subroutine DIVERT (Fig. 3.5)

(1) The unregulated flow for the river reach between all reservoirs and Bethlehem (the intermediate flow) is computed.

(2) The regulated flow at Bethlehem, being the sum of the intermediate flow and all the basic and supplementary releases, is computed.

(3) The Bethlehem regulated flow is compared to the water-supply target, whereupon 3 paths are available [steps (4), (5), or (6)].

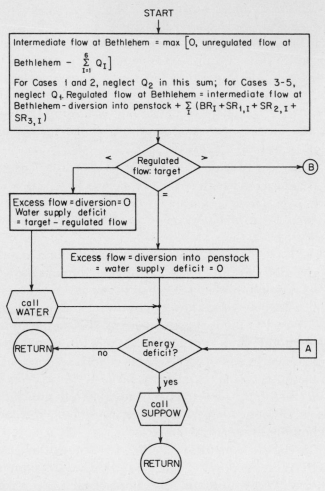

FIG. 3.5. Flow chart for subroutine DIVERT.

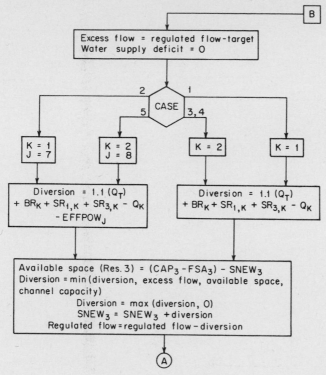

FIG. 3.5 (continued).

(4) If the Bethlehem regulated flow equals the target, the amount of water available for diversion and the water supply deficit are set to zero. Control advances to step (13).

(5) If the Bethlehem regulated flow is less than the target, the deficit is computed and control passes to Subroutine WATER for the allocation of second supplementary releases among the reservoirs. Upon return from Subroutine WATER, control advances to step (13).

(6) If the Bethlehem flow exceeds the target, the deficit is set to zero and the amount of water available for diversion is computed according to the following scheme.

(7) For *Case 1*, the amount available is the natural inflow between reservoirs 1 and 3 plus the basic and first supplementary releases (for minimum channel flows) from reservoir 1.

(8) For *Case 2*, the amount available is computed as in step (7)

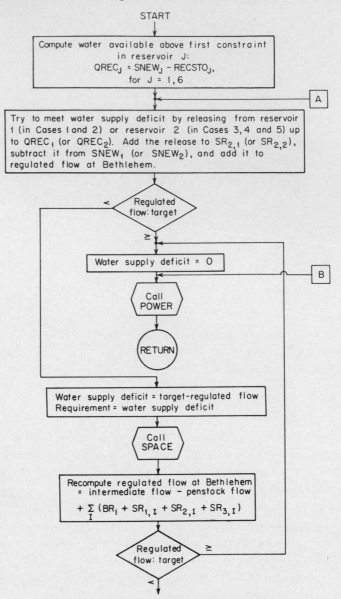

FIG. 3.6. Flow chart for subroutine WATER.

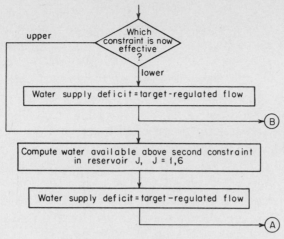

FIG. 3.6 (continued).

except that the effective power flow through turbine 7, or that quantity released to reservoir 4, is subtracted.

(9) For *Cases 3* and *4,* operation proceeds as in step (7) except that reservoir 2 appears for reservoir 1.

(10) For Case 5, operation proceeds as in steps (7) and (8), except that reservoir 2 and turbine 8 are applicable where reservoir 1 and turbine 7 appear.

(11) The amount actually diverted is limited by (i) the space available in reservoir 3, (ii) the capacity of the diversion works, or (iii) the difference between flow and target, whichever is smallest.

(12) The contents in reservoir 3 are incremented and the flow at Bethlehem is decremented by the amount diverted.

(13) If there is no energy deficit, control passes to the MAIN Program; if the energy deficit exceeds zero, Subroutine SUPPOW is called to allocate the third supplementary releases among the reservoirs, whereupon control returns from Subroutine DIVERT to the MAIN Program. The monthly algorithm is complete when the program returns to the MAIN Program from this subroutine.

Subroutine WATER (Fig. 3.6)

(1) For each reservoir, the surcharge (+) is defined as the quantity of water available above the first (i.e., upper) recreation constraint.

(2) For *Cases 1* and *2*, the attempt is made to meet the water-supply deficit by making the second supplementary release from reservoir 1. This release is limited by the surcharge at reservoir 1.

(3) For *Cases 3, 4,* and *5*, operation proceeds as in step (2) except that reservoir 2 is inserted where reservoir 1 appears.

(4) If this supplementary release satisfies the water deficit at Bethlehem, Subroutine POWER is called to evaluate the energy effects of the release, and control is returned to Subroutine DIVERT and, ultimately, to the MAIN Program.

(5) If additional releases are required, Subroutine SPACE is called to attempt to meet the deficit by making allocations from reservoirs 3–6. The new regulated flow at Bethlehem is computed and, if the water-supply target is met, control is transferred to step (4) and out of Subroutine WATER.

(6) If the water-supply target is not met, steps (1)–(5) are repeated, using the second (i.e., lower) recreation constraint as the level above which the surcharge (+) is defined. If the target cannot now be met, a shortage is noted. Subroutine POWER is called to evaluate the effects of releases, and control is returned to Subroutine DIVERT and ultimately to the MAIN Program.

Subroutine SUPPOW (Fig. 3.7)

(1) Subroutine POWER is called to evaluate the power generated by all releases in the system. If there is no energy deficit, control is returned to Subroutine DIVERT; otherwise operation continues with step (2).

(2) For each reservoir, the surcharge (+) is defined as the quantity of water available above the first recreation constraint.

(3) For each turbine, the usable turbine capacity is defined as the difference between the water capacity and the effective power flow.

(4) For each reservoir, the surcharge is compared to the usable turbine capacity. If the surcharge is greater, the constraint level is increased by the difference, thereby decreasing the surcharge to the level beyond which additional releases produce no incremental power.

(5) For *Cases 2, 4,* and *5*, the surcharges in reservoir 1 or 2 are further limited by the unused capacities of the penstocks supplying turbines 7, 9, and 8, respectively; any additional release is

routed downstream in the channel, bypassing the penstocks and turbines.

(6) A trial supplementary release is made from reservoir 1 (or 2). This release is routed through turbine 3, so the conditions in both reservoir 3 and reservoir 1 (or 2) must be examined to arrive at a reasonable approximation to the required flow; the release is limited by the surcharge in reservoir 1 (or 2).

(7) Subroutine POWER is called to evaluate the effects of the release made in step (6).

(8) The surcharge in reservoir 3 is limited by the newly computed unused turbine capacity, taking account of the release defined in step (6).

(9) The energy test is made; that is, a determination is made whether the generated energy meets the target within a specified tolerance. If so, control returns to Subroutine DIVERT, thence to the MAIN Program. If not, operation continues with step (10).

(10) If the energy deficit is negative, which implies too large a trial release, the release is reduced by an amount proportional to the excess, and control returns to step (7). Ultimately the energy test, step (9), is passed or the deficit is driven positive, whereupon the program continues with step (11).

(11) If the energy deficit is positive, the entire surcharge from reservoir 1 (or 2) is released. Subroutine POWER is called to evaluate the effect of this release, and if the deficit is negative, an acceptable release is approached as in steps (5)–(10). Otherwise, operation continues with step (12).

(12) If the energy deficit is still positive, additional releases are required from reservoirs 3–6. The average head and average generating time (time at or above dead storage) are computed for these reservoirs, and a trial requirement is evaluated which might satisfy the energy deficit.

(13) Subroutine SPACE is called to allocate releases among reservoirs 3–6 so that their sum equals the trial requirement.

(14) Updated surcharge (+) values are computed for reservoirs 3–6.

(15) Subroutine POWER is called to compute the energy generated by the system. Three branches are available [step (16), (17), or (18)].

(16) If the energy generated meets the energy target within the

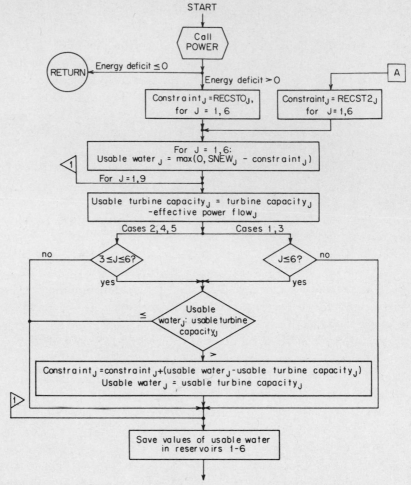

FIG. 3.7. Flow chart for subroutine SUPPOW.

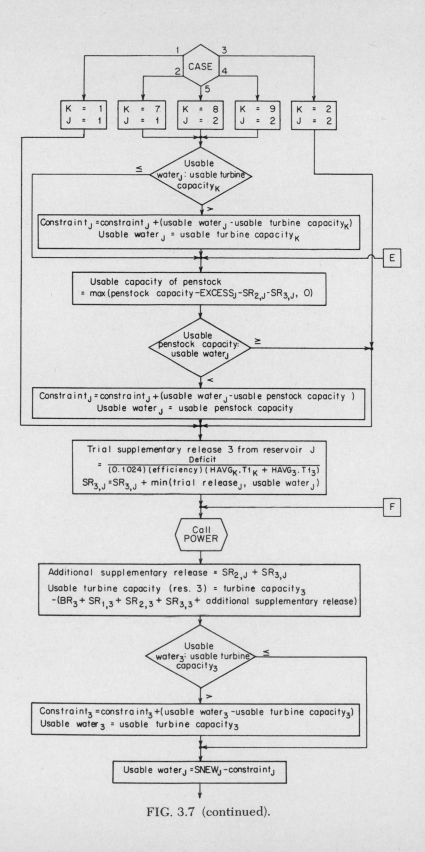

FIG. 3.7 (continued).

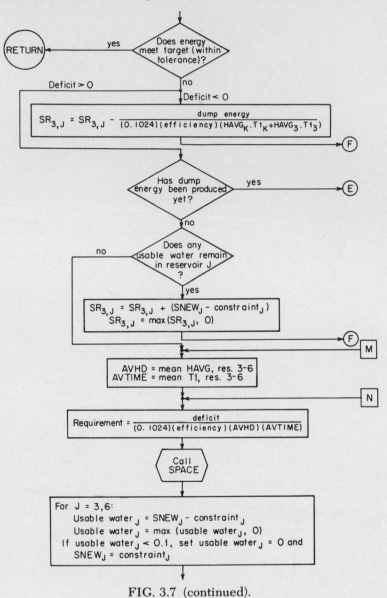

FIG. 3.7 (continued).

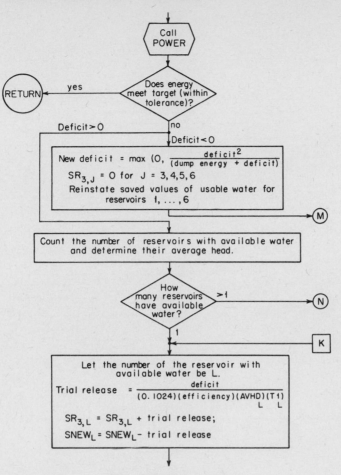

FIG. 3.7 (continued).

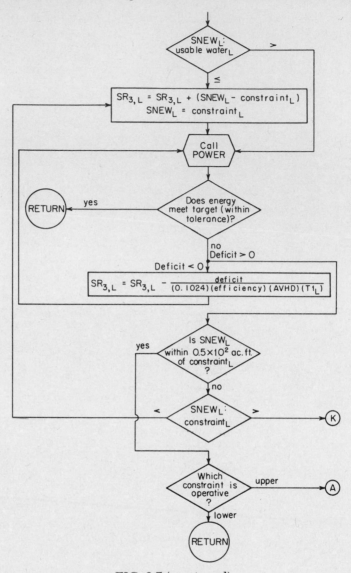

FIG. 3.7 (continued).

specified tolerance, control is returned to Subroutine DIVERT, thence to the MAIN Program.

(17) If the energy deficit is negative, the original state of the system is restored, a new (reduced) requirement is computed and control is returned to step (12).

(18) If the energy deficit is positive, the number of reservoirs for which the surcharge exceeds zero (i.e., from which additional releases may be made) is counted and a new average head is computed. If no reservoirs contain positive surcharges, control passes to step (25) or (26), depending on the constraint level in force.

(19) If the sum exceeds one, control returns to step (12) to compute a revised trial requirement.

(20) If the sum is one, an attempt is made to meet the requirement from the only remaining reservoir, noting that the magnitude of the release is limited by the surcharge (+).

(21) Subroutine POWER is called to compute the total energy generated.

(22) For each reservoir, the surcharge values are updated to account for the latest releases.

(23) If the energy generated meets the energy target within the specified tolerance, control returns to Subroutine DIVERT and thence to the MAIN Program.

(24) If the energy deficit is negative, the requirement is reduced and the original state of the system is restored; control then returns to step (21).

(25) If the energy deficit is still positive, it is necessary to replace the first recreational level constraint with the second and re-execute steps (2)–(24) because all the reservoirs are now drawn to their upper constraining levels.

(26) If an energy shortage still exists after the lower constraint is imposed, the shortage is noted and control returns to Subroutine DIVERT.

Subroutine SPACE (Fig. 3.8)

The basic release allocation equation referred to throughout is:

$$\text{Allocation}_j = \text{Contents}_j - \text{Capacity}_j + \frac{+\left[\Sigma_j(\text{Capacity}_j - \text{Contents}_j) + \text{Release Requirement}\right] \times \text{Future Inflow}_j}{\Sigma_j \text{Future Inflow}_j}$$

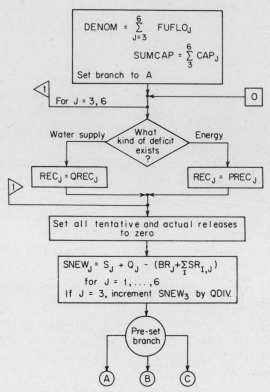

Fig. 3.8. Flow chart for subroutine SPACE.

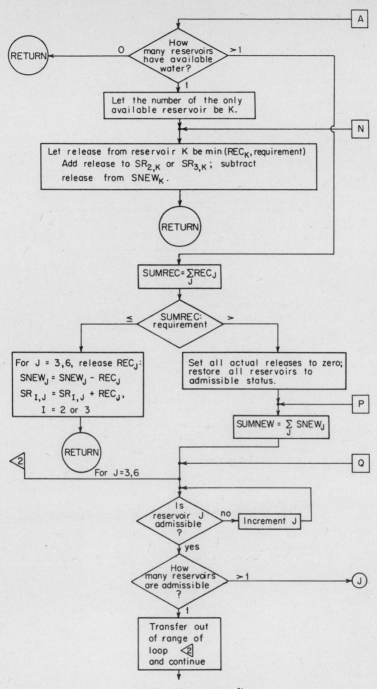

FIG. 3.8 (continued).

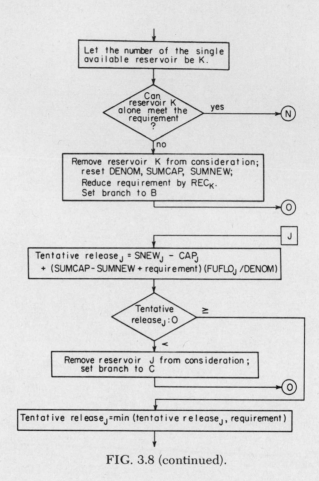

FIG. 3.8 (continued).

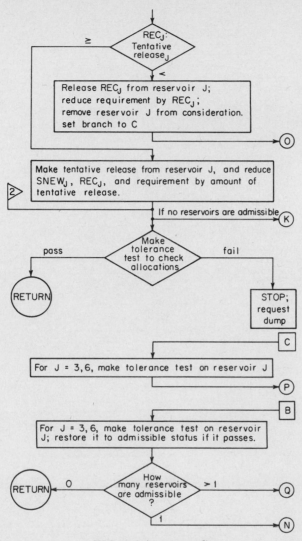

FIG. 3.8 (continued).

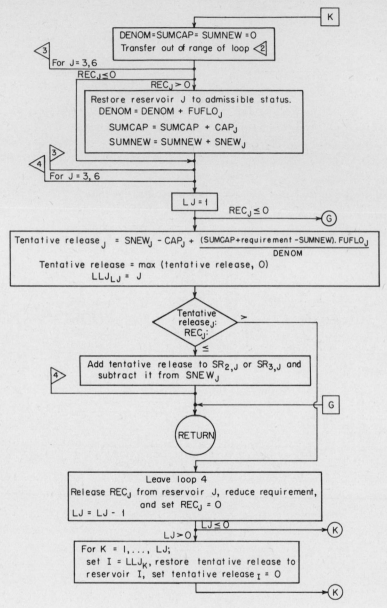

FIG. 3.8 (continued).

where J is the reservoir number and the summations are performed over $J = 3, 4, 5, 6$.

(1) The value Σ_J (Future Inflow)$_J$ is computed where the argument is an input vector which reflects the expected inflows from the current month to the end of the drawdown-refill cycle.

(2) The value Σ_J Capacity$_J$ is computed and the magnitude of the externally specified release requirement is noted.

(3) The relevant surcharge (+) values are computed depending upon the origin of the requirement (i.e., whether there exists an energy or water-supply deficit). Note that the effects of turbine and recreation constraints are considered in the calling routine, not in Subroutine SPACE.

(4) All reservoir contents are updated.

(5) The number of reservoirs in which the surcharge exceeds zero are counted. Three paths are available [step (6), (7), or (8)]:

(6) If the sum is zero, control returns to the calling location since no gain can be effected by continuing in this subroutine.

(7) If the sum is one, the required release is made from the corresponding reservoir (limited by the surcharge), the reservoir contents are decremented accordingly, and control returns to the calling location.

(8) If the sum exceeds one, the feasibility of further computation is tested by summing the four surcharges and comparing the sum to the requirement.

(9) If the sum of surcharges is equal to or less than the requirement, all the surcharges are released, all reservoir contents are decremented, and control returns to the calling location. Otherwise, control continues with step (10).

(10) If the sum of surcharges exceeds the requirement, control remains in this subroutine until the requirement is satisfied. The value Σ_J Contents$_J$ is computed for substitution into the basic release allocation equation.

(11) For each reservoir in turn, starting with reservoir 3, the test is made to determine whether the reservoir remains a member of the set of admissible sources of water. An admissible source is one (a) with a positive surcharge value and (b) with a non-negative tentative release allocation. The first time this step is executed, all reservoirs are admissible as all have positive surcharge values and zero tentative release allocations.

(12) If a reservoir is no longer admissible, the next reservoir number is considered in sequence and control returns to step (11) until all reservoirs are completed. When all 4 reservoirs are examined, control transfers to step (19).

(13) If a reservoir is admissible, a test is made to determine whether it is the only admissible reservoir.

(14a) If only one reservoir is admissible, a test is made to determine if its surcharge is adequate to meet the requirement. If so, control goes to step (7) [entry (N), Fig. 3.8] to make the necessary releases. If not, its surcharge is released, and control returns to execute step (3) only [entry (O), Fig. 3.8], thereafter transferring control to step (14b).

(14b) If all reservoirs are drawn down to their constraint levels, control returns to the calling location.

(14c) If one reservoir remains unutilized, control goes to step (7) to withdraw the required surcharge.

(14d) If more than one reservoir remains unutilized, control goes to step (11) and the allocation is started anew [entry (J), Fig. 3.8].

(15) If no reservoirs are admissible [entry (K), Fig. 3.8] the surcharges for all 4 reservoirs are computed and the computation begins anew by releasing from those reservoirs with positive surcharge values. This step is rarely reached; indeed, extreme combinations of input data are required to induce the enormous imbalance in allocations implicit in reaching this step. Finally, control returns to the calling location.

(16) If more than one reservoir is admissible, allocations are made in accordance with the basic release allocation equation given above.

(17) If an allocated release exceeds the associated surcharge, only the surcharge is released. Then the requirement is reduced and the reservoir contents updated; this reservoir, fully utilized, is now withdrawn from the set of admissible reservoirs [entry (O), Fig. 3.8]. The values $\Sigma_J(\text{Future Inflow})_J$, $\Sigma_J\text{Capacity}_J$, and $\Sigma_J\text{Contents}_J$ are recomputed, and the allocation begins anew at step (11).

(19) After all allocations are made, their sum is compared to the original requirement to ascertain that no continuity error is made. If an error is detected, the routine stops and requests a memory dump; otherwise, control is returned to the calling location.

THE FLOOD ALGORITHM

General Statement

The Flood Algorithm consists of two portions. The generating portion, contained in Subroutine FGEN, is called by the MAIN Program in each month of the simulation; its functions are to perform a set of regressions on the monthly discharge values at reservoir sites 1–6, Bethlehem, and Walnutport, and thereby to estimate the 3-hour flood peaks at the zones of potential flood damage. If any estimated peak exceeds the associated channel capacity, the routing sequence, contained in Subroutines HYDRO, ROUTER, and FSPACE, is initiated by Subroutine FGEN. In any case, control is returned to the MAIN Program from Subroutine FGEN.

= Muskingum method.

The routing routines utilize the modified Gilchrist method and combine 3-hour flows at 8 sites (6 reservoirs, Bethlehem, and Walnutport) and at 2 intermediate zones to synthesize the regulated and unregulated discharges at Walnutport and at Bethlehem. The reservoir operating rules which prevail during flood periods are simple. When a flood is imminent, an attempt is made to maintain each reservoir at its flood storage level; if this induces flows which exceed the channel capacities below one or more reservoirs or which cause a damaging flood at the downstream damage zones (Walnutport or Bethlehem), the reservoirs are allowed to fill above their long-term storage levels (i.e., to encroach upon the flood-storage allowance). If a reservoir fills, the spill or inevitable flow is routed downstream along with any regular release already made during that 3-hour interval.[3]

In the event of an historical analysis, the flood data provided on magnetic tape consist of 3-hour flood flows at the several sites. Thus, the generating portion of the Flood Algorithm can be skipped, and control is immediately transferred to Subroutine ROUTER.

Subroutine FGEN

This subroutine is called by the MAIN Program after the Monthly Algorithm is executed. Reference is made to Fig. 3.9 for identification and notation.

---

[3] The effect of temporary storage above the spillway crest is not included in the program, but coding and inserting the relevant instructions should pose no major problems.

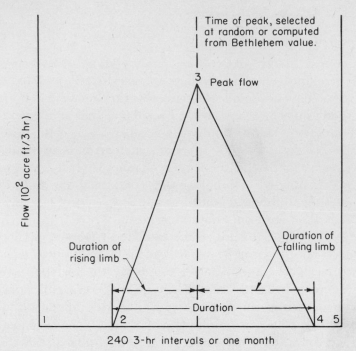

Fig. 3.9. Form of synthetic flood hydrograph generated by subroutine FGEN.

(1) The time-of-peak for Bethlehem is established by drawing a random integer between 1 and 240 (there are 240 3-hour time periods per month); from this value the peaks at the 6 reservoir sites and at Walnutport are computed by subtracting the relevant time of travel or time lag.

(2) Then, for each of the 6 reservoir sites, for Bethlehem, and for Walnutport, the following computations are performed:

(a) The peak flow is estimated by a linear regression on monthly discharge. Under input control, the regression is based on the untransformed data or on data subjected to a logarithmic transform; thus a normal or log-normal bivariate distribution of flood peaks and monthly discharges is predicated. The model includes a random additive component, and the applicable generating equation, for a particular site and month, is either of the following:

$$P = \mu_P + \beta(Q - \mu_Q) + \sigma(1 - \rho^2)^{1/2}t, \tag{1}$$
$$P = \exp[\bar{\mu}_P + \bar{\beta}(\log Q - \bar{\mu}_Q) + \bar{\sigma}(1 - \bar{\rho}^2)^{1/2}t], \tag{2}$$

where

P, Q are the generated peak and monthly flows, respectively;

β, ρ are the regression and correlation coefficients between peak and monthly flows;

σ is the standard deviation of peak flows;

μ_P, μ_Q are the arithmetic means of the peak and monthly flows;

t is a standard normal deviate of zero mean and unit variance; and

$\bar{\mu}_P, \bar{\mu}_Q, \bar{\beta}, \bar{\rho}, \bar{\sigma}$ are the equivalent parameters of the logarithmically transformed data.

Any negative peak is arbitrarily incremented to zero, thereby introducing an error into the validity of the model. Since this error occurs for small values of the peak P, it cannot affect those values which are of interest to the Flood Algorithm; accordingly, our simplification is warranted. Our studies show that the logarithmic transform, (ii) above, is more nearly representative of the hydrologic regime in the Lehigh River. All subsequent references to generating peak flows from monthly discharges, then, pertain to the transformed equation (2).

(b) The duration (Fig. 3.9) is estimated as a linear function of peak flow and monthly discharge. Because the independent variates are strongly correlated (i.e., peak and discharge exhibit significant correlation), the traditional least-squares regression technique is not applicable. In its place we substitute a multivariate (principal component) analysis in which the historical durations, taken from the flood hydrographs, are arrayed against the two orthogonal components formed from linear blends of the "independent" variates (peak and discharge). An alternative regression function, duration versus the principal components, is defined; this function is an alternative to the multivariate least-squares analysis whose validity rests on independence among the arguments. No data transforms are utilized in this regression technique because the paucity of data renders any one distribution as valid as any other.

(c) The duration is divided into a rising and falling portion in accordance with a scheme which utilizes a random number drawn from a rectangular distribution of random numbers in the range 0–1.

Each month and each site are characterized by a pair of fractions, both less than unity, such that the portion of the duration represented by the rising limb lies between the two fractions. For example, if the two limiting data are 0.3 and 0.5, the rising limb accounts for between 30 and 50 percent of the total duration, and, moreover, is rectangularly (uniformly) distributed in that range. Thus a random number suffices to fix the rising limb uniquely; for example, a random number of 0.45 implies a rising limb of 0.30 + 0.45 (0.50 − 0.30) or 39 percent of the total duration.

(d) The volume subtended by the triangular flood wedge [points (2), (3), and (4) in Fig. 3.9] is compared to the monthly discharge. If the flood volume exceeds the monthly flow, point (2) is increased and point (4) is decreased by 0.5 time units, thereby decreasing the duration by one unit, or 3 hours, until the volumes are brought into agreement or until the duration reaches 6 time-intervals, or 18 hours, whereupon the program accepts the inconsistency and continues the computation. On the other hand, if the monthly discharge exceeds the flood volume, no adjustment is made.

(e) If points (2) and (4) or Fig. 3.9 lie outside the range 1–240, the entire flood wedge is shifted as necessary so that the flood is contained within a single calendar month.

(3) The peak flows at Walnutport and Bethlehem are compared to the respective channel capacities; if neither peak exceeds the associated capacity, the program returns control to the MAIN Program. If either or both peaks exceeds the capacity, the program continues with step (4).

(4) Two sites are created, viz., intermediate flow above Walnutport and intermediate flow between Walnutport and Bethlehem. The peaks at these sites are estimated by subtractions:

$$P'_W = P_W - P_1 - P_2 - P_3 - P_4 - P_5 \tag{3}$$

and

$$P'_B = P_B - P_W - P_6, \tag{4}$$

where

P'_W, P'_B are the intermediate peaks above Walnutport and Bethlehem, respectively;

P_i is the peak at reservoir site i ($i = 1$ to 6); and

P_W, P_B are the peaks at Walnutport and Bethlehem respectively.

In this computation P_1 and P_2 cannot jointly be positive because reservoirs 1 and 2 are alternatives; thus, when P_1 is considered, $P_2 = 0$, and conversely.

(5) The flood hydrographs derived for Bethlehem and Walnutport, or the three points which characterize these hydrographs, are now discarded because the Bethlehem and Walnutport flow patterns are synthesized from routed flows which originate at the 6 reservoir sites and at the 2 intermediate sites. This is the function of Subroutine HYDRO, to which Subroutine FGEN transfers control at this point.

(6) Following the construction of the natural flow hydrographs in Subroutine HYDRO, control is transferred to Subroutine ROUTER for supervision of the 3-hourly releases which are made during the flood period. Thereafter, control is returned to the MAIN Program.

Subroutine HYDRO

This subroutine connects the 5 points of each site's hydrograph by straight line segments and routes the flows from the 6 dam sites and 2 intermediate zones in order to synthesize natural or unregulated flood hydrographs at Walnutport and Bethlehem.

(1) For the 6 dam sites and 2 intermediate zones, 3-hourly flows are interpolated from line segments constructed between successive pairs of points, (2)–(3) and (3)–(4) in Fig. 3.9.

(2) The flows at reservoir sites 1–5 are routed to Walnutport using the modified Gilchrist method. By accumulating these 5 component flows and the unregulated intermediate flow above Walnutport, the total Walnutport flow is synthesized.

(3) The 3-hourly flow at Bethlehem is synthesized by routing the flows from reservoir 6 and from Walnutport to Bethlehem, and adding together the unregulated intermediate flow between Walnutport and Bethlehem. The new peaks at Walnutport and Bethlehem generally do not equal the original peaks calculated by linear regression. It is unfortunate that estimates based on these strong correlations are not preserved for use in the routing analyses, but clearly it is impossible to preserve the generated peaks at Bethlehem and Walnutport without overdetermining the flows from the upstream zones. To avoid any inconsistency, the original Bethlehem and Walnutport peaks are discarded and recalculated from the constituent flows.

(4) Control is returned to Subroutine FGEN, which in turn immediately transfers control to Subroutine ROUTER.

Subroutine ROUTER

This subroutine supervises the operation of the 6 reservoirs in the Lehigh System during flood events. Two types of flood are encountered. Type 1 floods, if unregulated by the storage facilities in the system, would produce damage at Bethlehem or Walnutport, or both, but produce no damage when regulated; Type 2 floods are damaging even when regulated, although some attenuation is obtained unless all reservoirs in the entire system are full when the peak inflow arrives at the dams. Subroutine ROUTER makes 3-hourly releases starting at the earliest flood time, T', to the latest flood time, T''.

(1) The reservoir contents at the start of the month are assumed to obtain at time T'. For each 3-hour time increment in the range T' to T''', steps (2)–(7) are performed.

(2) The excess channel capacity at Walnutport is computed by subtracting from the channel capacity the regulated flow for the preceding time interval. For time period T', the first in the sequence, the regulated flow is arbitrarily equated to the natural flow in the preceding interval. If the excess capacity is not positive, no flood release is made from reservoirs 1–5 unless a reservoir is forced to spill; in general, the routine attempts to store the entire inflow.

If the excess channel capacity is positive, the cumulative available storage (above the flood-storage levels) in all reservoirs is computed and compared to the available channel capacity. If the capacity exceeds the available release, all reservoirs are drawn to their respective flood-storage levels. A hedging factor (≥ 1.0) enables additional releases to be made at the reservoirs because the flood wave is attenuated during translation and the resulting increment of flow at Walnutport is slightly less than the sum of the incremental releases.

(3) If the available flow exceeds the capacity, the water in storage exceeds the channel capacity at Walnutport, and some reservoir or reservoirs are not drawn down to the flood-storage level. Subroutine FSPACE is called to supervise the allocation of releases.

(4) The release from each reservoir 1–5 is routed to Walnutport

using the modified Gilchrist method and is added to the unregulated inflow above Walnutport, thereby producing the total regulated flow at Walnutport.

(5) In precisely the same fashion, the release from reservoir 6 is constrained by the Bethlehem channel capacity. Recourse to Subroutine FSPACE is not necessary because allocation of releases among several reservoirs is not required; the routed release from reservoir 6, the routed regulated flow at Walnutport, and the natural inflow between Walnutport and Bethlehem comprise the flow at Bethlehem. Thus the excess storage at reservoir 6 is compared to the channel capacity. If the capacity exceeds the excess storage available in reservoir 6, the reservoir is lowered to its flood-storage level; otherwise, an amount equal to the available capacity is released. The release from reservoir 6 and the flow at Walnutport are routed to Bethlehem and added to the unregulated flow between Walnutport and Bethlehem, thereby producing the total regulated flow at Bethlehem.

(6) The flow reductions at Walnutport and at Bethlehem are computed by subtracting the regulated from the unregulated flows at each site; the largest reduction in peak for each month at each site is preserved and utilized in the benefit analyses.

(7) If the channel capacity exceeds the regulated flow at Walnutport and conversely at Bethlehem, reductions in releases from reservoirs 1–5 might enable the Bethlehem flow to be contained within the channel. In this event the damaging portion of the Bethlehem flow is subtracted from the allowable flow at Walnutport, defining a new, reduced channel capacity; thereupon the routing process begins anew at time T' [step (4)].

If the excess channel capacity at Walnutport becomes negative by virtue of the subtraction, it is set to zero and damages are necessarily suffered at Bethlehem.

(8) For all 6 reservoirs, the program inquires whether the end-of-month contents specified by the Monthly Algorithm can be attained while respecting the constraint that no release shall exceed the channel capacity downstream from each site. If it is impossible to reach the terminal storage, the final storage computed in this step overrides the earlier value.

(9) Control is returned to the MAIN Program.

Subroutine FSPACE

When there is more water above the long-term storage levels in reservoirs 1, 2, 4, and 5 than can be accommodated in the channel at Walnutport, Subroutine ROUTER calls Subroutine FSPACE to make the appropriate allocation of releases. Reservoirs 3 and 6 are not considered by the allocation algorithm. Reservoir 3 is treated separately from the rest because it can be filled by diversions from releases made upstream at either reservoir 1 or 2; thus the program assures that reservoir 3 is drawn down to the flood-storage level (assuming adequate channel capacity at the site and at Walnutport) before attempting any allocated releases from the remaining reservoirs. And, since releases from reservoir 6 enter the channel between Walnutport and Bethlehem, releases therefrom are not relevant to the allocation problem above Walnutport.

Since reservoirs 1 and 2 are alternatives, only one can appear in any allocation problem; thus Subroutine FSPACE must deal with 3 reservoirs only: 1 (or 2), 4, and 5. For ease of indexing, Subroutine FSPACE assigns the temporary identifying numbers I, II, and III to reservoirs 1 (or 2), 4, and 5, respectively.

(1) The water available for release from reservoir 3 is limited by the channel capacity below the site. The available flow, thus constrained, is compared to the remaining channel capacity at Walnutport. If the remaining capacity exceeds the available flow, the entire available volume is released from reservoir 3 and the program proceeds to step (2) to consider the reduced channel capacity. If the flow exceeds the capacity, that portion of the available flow is released which just fills the channel at Walnutport, whereupon control is returned to Subroutine ROUTER.

(2) If an allocation is required from reservoirs I, II, and III, the program executes exactly the same iterative scheme incorporated in Subroutine SPACE, Monthly Algorithm. The flow requirement, an argument of the subroutine, is here defined as the volume of flow which just fills the channel at Walnutport; this is analogous to the volume of flow required to meet a water supply or power deficit in the Monthly Algorithm. Execution of Subroutine FSPACE demands less time than that for Subroutine SPACE because there are 3 instead of 4 reservoirs from which releases can be made, but the basic allocation rule used in both subroutines is, in all respects, identical. One significant detail is changed in Subroutine FSPACE.

Instead of apportioning releases to accord with the expected inflows between the current month and the end of the drawdown-refill cycle, as in Subroutine SPACE, Subroutine FSPACE apportions releases to accord with the 3-hourly inflow in the next time-interval, or 3-hour period. After making the appropriate releases, control is returned to Subroutine ROUTER and the next interval is considered.

BENEFIT AND COST ANALYSES

Analyses of the economic consequences of system operation—the benefits and costs—proceed through use of the *Monthly Benefit*, *Annual Benefit*, and *Run Benefit* algorithms, after initialization is performed in Subroutine SETUPB. As shown in Fig. 3.1, the general flow chart, Subroutine SETUPB is called at the start of each study to set the cost and benefit accumulators to their initial values. As described earlier, the Monthly Benefit Algorithm, contained in Subroutine BENACM, is called at the end of each month of system operation to evaluate monthly performance in economic terms. At the end of each year the Annual Benefit Algorithm, contained in Subroutine BENACY, accumulates and evaluates annual benefits; finally, at the conclusion of each demand period, the Run Benefit Algorithm, contained in Subroutines BENDYN and COST, accumulates, edits, and discounts benefit and cost values for the entire demand period. If another demand period remains to be analyzed, Subroutine SETUPB is recalled to prepare for the ensuing study; if all demand periods of a study have been examined, the program proceeds to the next study and, if all studies in the job have been examined, the program terminates.

The Monthly Benefit Algorithm
(Subroutine BENACM)

This subroutine is called each month by the MAIN Program after all the operating algorithms (Hydrology, Monthly, and Flood) are completed.

(1) If an energy deficit exists for the month, the cumulative deficit (in mwhr) for the year and a deficit counter are incremented. If the deficit exceeds 25 percent of the monthly target, a separate counter is incremented.

(2) Energy (in mwhr) required for pumping from reservoir 1 or 2 to the Beltzville pipe is computed.

(3) Dump energy (in mwhr) is accumulated.

(4) The excess of deficiency of water supply (in 10^2 acre ft) is accumulated.

(5) When energy or water supply deficits exist, they are evaluated in dollars by use of cubic loss-functions (see Fig. 2.33), and the results are accumulated.

(6) Dump-energy benefits are evaluated in dollars and accumulated.

(7) The energy cost for pumping is computed and subtracted from dump-energy benefits.

(8) Recreation losses for the month are evaluated and accumulated. For each reservoir in turn, a linear relationship between storage and time is assumed. If the storage never falls below the upper recreation constraint level, that is if the initial and final storage values equal or exceed the constraint, there is no recreation loss. If, however, either the initial or final storage levels, or both, lie below the constraint, the proportion of the month during which storage is below the recreation level is computed. By integrating a polynomial loss function (see Fig. 2.35) over the relevant time span, and by obtaining the product of visitor-days and value per visitor-day, the recreation loss in dollars is found for each reservoir; in this manner, the total recreation loss for the system is computed.

(9) If the unregulated flow produces no flooding at Bethlehem and Walnutport, all flood benefits are set to zero and control returns to the MAIN Program.

(10) If the unregulated flows produce flooding but the regulated flows do not, flood benefits at Bethlehem, Walnutport, and the stream-reaches below reservoirs 4, 5, and 6 are taken as the damages associated with unregulated flows. These are evaluated by means of polynomials whose arguments are the unregulated flows (see Figs. 2.30 to 2.32 for the relevant discharge-damage functions).

(11) Finally, if the unregulated and regulated flow both result in flooding, flood benefits for each site or reach are computed by subtracting damages suffered with regulation from damages without regulation. Both classes of damage are computed by means of the polynomials mentioned in step (10) above.

(12) Control is returned to the MAIN Program.

The Annual Benefit Algorithm
(Subroutine BENACY)

This subroutine computes benefits on a yearly basis, and performs appropriate discounting computations in the event of a discounted run. The routine is called by the MAIN Program at the completion of each year of the simulation.

(1) The annual energy benefit in dollars, i.e., nominal annual benefit plus accumulated dump benefits less accumulated losses, is computed. The accumulating registers are cleared.

(2) The annual water-supply and recreation benefits in dollars, i.e. nominal values less accumulated losses, are computed. The accumulating registers are cleared.

(3) Three types of flood values are defined (in dollars):
- (a) annual flood damages prevented (called annual flood prevention benefits);
- (b) annual flood damages sustained (called annual residual flood damages); and
- (c) annual flood damages which would have been sustained in the absence of regulation (called potential flood damages).

All monthly accumulating registers are cleared.

(4) The following quantities and their squares are accumulated:
- (a) annual dump energy, mwhr;
- (b) annual energy shortage, mwhr;
- (c) annual energy benefit, dollars;
- (d) annual water supply benefit, dollars;
- (e) annual recreation benefit, dollars;
- (f) annual flood prevention benefit, dollars;
- (g) annual residual flood damages, dollars;
- (h) annual potential flood damages, dollars.

(5) The annual gross benefit, given by (c) + (d) + (e) + (f), is computed and accumulated from year to year; likewise, its square is computed and accumulated. In addition, annual non-flood benefits (c), (d) and (e) are summed and annual residual flood damages (g) are subtracted; this value and its square are accumulated. For an undiscounted run, control is returned to the MAIN Program, but for a discounted run the program continues to steps (6) and (7).

(6) The annual energy, water-supply, recreation and flood-prevention benefits are discounted by applying the factor $1/(1+r)^i$ where i is the current year in the simulation sequence and r, the discount rate, attains values of 0, 2, $2\frac{1}{2}$, 3, $3\frac{1}{2}$ ..., 6 percent. The discounted values are accumulated in registers corresponding to each value of r.

(7) Similarly, the squares of the annual discounted benefits for the various purposes are computed and added to the appropriate registers. Control then returns to the MAIN Program.

The Run Benefit Algorithm

Subroutine BENDYN

This subroutine is called at the end of each demand period. For a discounted run, it merely performs a small amount of routine bookkeeping prior to calling the Output Algorithm. For an undiscounted run, however, this subroutine computes the mean and standard deviation of the accumulated annual benefits and then applies the necessary discount factor to these quantities.

(1) For an *undiscounted* run, the factors which convert mean annual benefits and the standard deviation of annual benefits to present values are computed for the array of 10 interest rates. These factors are:

Factor for conversion of means equals

$$\sum_{i=M_1}^{M_2} \frac{1}{(1+r)^i},$$

Factor for conversion of standard deviations equals

$$\sum_{i=M_1}^{M_2} \frac{1}{(1+r)^{2i}},$$

where M_1 is the first year of the demand period, and
M_2 is the last year of the demand period.

(2) For an *undiscounted* run, the mean and standard deviation of the annual benefits are computed. For each interest rate, these moments are discounted to present value using the conversion factors computed in step (1).

(3) As an aid to comparing hydrologic input data with system outputs the first 4 moments and the relevant correlation coefficients (i.e., serial and cross) are computed from the data comprising the input hydrology. Note that if the input hydrology is historical data, the moments are those of the actual record which can then be used as input to an operational hydrology generator in a subsequent study.

(4) For both *discounted* and *undiscounted* runs, Subroutine COST is called to compute capital and OMR costs of input variables, and the Output Algorithm is called to write on magnetic tape the moments of the hydrologic inputs, and summaries of the input variables, costs, and benefits. Subroutine SETUPB is then recalled to initialize the benefit accumulators for subsequent runs.

Subroutine COST

This subroutine proceeds as follows:

(1) All capital and OMR cost registers are initialized.

(2) Capital costs of reservoirs 1–6 are computed by means of polynomials whose arguments are total storage capacity. (See Figs. 2.13 and 2.14 for these functions.)

(3) OMR costs of all reservoirs are computed by means of a single polynomial whose argument is the reservoir capital cost. (See Fig. 2.20 for this function.)

(4) Capital costs of power plants 1–6 are computed as the sum of (1) the penstock costs, which are functions of power plant capacity (see Fig. 2.16), and (2) turbine and generator costs, which are functions of the size of power plant and rated head (see Fig. 2.15).

(5) Similarly, capital costs for power plants 7, 8, and 9 are computed as the sum of (1) the costs of the high head Beltzville or Lehigh pipes and auxiliary facilities which are functions of installed power plant capacity (see Figs. 2.17 and 2.18) and (2) turbine and generator costs as computed above.

(6) OMR costs for power plants are computed as a function of installed capacity (see Fig. 2.21).

(7) Capital cost of specific recreation facilities for each reservoir is computed as a function of annual recreation capacity of the reservoir in visitor-days. This is itself a function of the reservoir storage level for which the recreation facilities are designed (see Fig. 2.19 for these functions).

(8) OMR costs of specific recreation facilities are computed as a function of capital costs.

(9) All capital cost data are checked to determine if they relate to a reservoir that was constructed in a previous demand period; if so, all such capital costs are set to zero.

(10) All capital and all OMR costs are accumulated.

(11) Control returns to Subroutine BENDYN.

THE OUTPUT ALGORITHM

The Output Algorithm is called at the end of each demand period to print physical and economic data that are either provided as input or generated by the simulation. As shown in Table 3.1, the first section (A) of printed output presents the statistical characteristics of the monthly flows used in the simulation analysis. Section (B) of the table lists flood-flow data, including flood peaks generated by the simulation, and unregulated and regulated flows, routed as required, at reservoirs and damage zones.

Sections (C) and (D) present the values of the major design variables, all of which are inputs to the simulation, along with the capital and OMR costs of the reservoirs, power plants, and recreational facilities.

In the next output section (E), physical performance of the system is summarized by showing maximal and minimal contents and stationary-state distributions of storage for all reservoirs, the number of floods, maximal flood peaks with and without regulation, cumulative energy surpluses and cumulative deficits for energy, water-supply and recreation outputs.

Section (E) also presents economic data. For an undiscounted run [portrayed in Table 3.1(E)], the mean and standard deviation of annual energy, water-supply, and flood-prevention benefits, and of annual flood damages with and without the system, are shown. In addition, the mean annual benefits for all purposes other than flood prevention less mean annual flood damages (1) with the system and (2) without the system are listed. For a discounted run, the stream of annual benefits and flood damages, discounted from the year of occurrence of each element to year 1 of the study at each of 10 discount rates, is displayed. [These data are not shown in Table 3.1(E)]

For all runs, discounted or undiscounted, cumulative costs and benefits, reduced to present value at the 10 discount rates, are presented as shown in section (F) of the table. For the first demand period of each study, these cumulative costs and benefits are simply the discounted costs incurred and benefits attained during the period; however, for each subsequent demand period in the study, the cumulated costs and benefits of preceding demand periods are added to the costs and benefits of the current demand period, all discounted to the first year of the entire study. Thus the cumulative costs and benefits reported for the final demand period of any study provide the relevant economic summary for the entire study. In fact, the last column (labeled net benefits) of the cumulative cost and benefit display for the final demand period comprises the payoff, in present value of net benefits, at 10 discount rates, for the system design under investigation.

SERVICE ROUTINES

Subroutine GM

At several points we have referred to a spline curve fitting technique; all such references pertain to Subroutine GM.[4] Many arrays of empirical data, such as the relationships between height and storage behind each reservoir, between flood damage and discharge, or between the energy deficit and energy loss, are approximated by a set of third-degree polynomials, each of which pertains to a particular range of the argument or independent variable. The largest number of polynomials required to fit our empirical functions is four. The segments are continuous and continuously differentiable at their junctions, so that the resulting function is a smooth curve or spline.

Using the coefficients derived by the spline curve-fitting technique, Subroutine GM examines the magnitude of each argument to determine which segment of the spline is required, and then evaluates the polynomial using the coefficients appropriate to that segment. Eight subroutines of the Lehigh simulation program utilize Subroutine GM for evaluation of polynomial functions.

[4] This curve-fitting technique, developed by the Research Laboratories of the General Motors Corporation, was made available to us through the kindness of that Laboratory and Dr. Carl de Boor.

TABLE 3.1. Output block.

(A) The statistical characteristics of the monthly flows are tabulated for runs with historical or synthetic data. The nine columns correspond to reservoirs 1–6, Walnutport, Bethlehem, and Tannery, respectively. Values for column 7 are zero because the monthly operation ignores Walnutport flows. Five rows are required for each month starting with January; the parameters (rows) are mean, standard deviation, skewness coefficient, kurtosis coefficient, and correlation coefficient. For reservoirs 1 and 2 the flows are proportional to Tannery; hence the correlations are perfect. Reservoirs 3–6 are correlated with Bethlehem, and the lag one serial correlations appear for Bethlehem and Tannery. All flows are in units of 10^2 acre ft.

0.3543E 01	0.3543E 01	0.3146E 01	0.3712E 01	0.2586E 01	0.2867E 01	-0.	0.3084E 01	0.3543E 01
0.1000E 01	0.1000E 01	0.9265E 00	0.9442E 00	0.9722E 00	0.8948E 00	0.	0.3664E-00	0.2832E-00
0.1746E 03	0.2248E 03	0.3284E 02	0.6137E 02	0.6258E 02	0.3026E 02	0.	0.9004E 03	0.2512E 03
0.1454E 03	0.1872E 03	0.2905E 02	0.5258E 02	0.5404E 02	0.2259E 02	-0.	0.6939E 03	0.2091E 03
0.4021E-00	0.4021E-00	0.6386E 00	0.7229E 00	0.6480E 00	0.5223E 00	0.	0.2108E-00	0.4021E-00
0.1905E 01	0.1905E 01	0.2588E 01	0.2891E 01	0.2848E 01	0.2617E 01	-0.	0.1974E 01	0.1905E 01
0.1000E 01	1.0000E 00	0.9401E 00	0.9464E 00	0.8723E 00	0.7972E 00	0.	0.5853E 00	0.6163E 00
0.1448E 03	0.1864E 03	0.2709E 02	0.5201E 02	0.5198E 02	0.2622E 02	0.	0.7733E 03	0.2083E 03
0.1311E 03	0.1688E 03	0.1935E 02	0.4623E 02	0.5557E 02	0.2463E 02	-0.	0.5981E 03	0.1886E 03

(A) Continued

0.5273E 00	0.4789E-00	0.	0.5956E 00	0.9169E 00	0.8718E 00	0.3165E-00	0.5274E 00	0.5273E 00
0.2236E 01	0.2191E 01	-0.	0.2187E 01	0.2630E 01	0.3021E 01	0.2195E 01	0.2236E 01	0.2236E 01
0.3942E-00	0.3728E-00	0.	0.8968E 00	0.8078E 00	0.9156E 00	0.8485E 00	1.0000E 00	1.0000E 00
0.2108E 00	0.7409E 03	0.	0.2495E 02	0.4712E 02	0.3975E 02	0.2410E 02	0.1887E 03	0.1465E 03
0.1528E 03	0.5540E 03	-0.	0.1983E 02	0.4017E 02	0.3340E 02	0.1828E 02	0.1368E 03	0.1062E 03
0.2157E-00	0.4455E-00	0.	0.7934E 00	0.6274E 00	0.7152E 00	0.4332E-00	0.2157E-00	0.2157E-00
0.2061E 01	0.2249E 01	-0.	0.2988E 01	0.2249E 01	0.3002E 01	0.2347E 01	0.2061E 01	0.2061E 01
0.2796E-00	0.5299E 00	0.	0.8977E 00	0.9149E 00	0.7882E 00	0.7299E 00	0.1000E 01	1.0000E 00
0.2861E 03	0.8751E 03	-0.	0.2266E 02	0.4914E 02	0.5248E 02	0.2449E 02	0.2560E 03	0.1988E 03
0.2152E 03	0.6063E 03	0.	0.2393E 02	0.3811E 02	0.3874E 02	0.2209E 02	0.1926E 03	0.1496E 03
0.4384E-00	0.7718E 00	0.	0.1279E 01	0.7323E 00	0.1109E 01	0.1108E 01	0.4384E-00	0.4384E-00
0.2418E 01	0.3587E 01	-0.	0.4681E 01	0.3081E 01	0.4909E 01	0.3919E 01	0.2418E 01	0.2418E 01
0.2717E-00	0.1636E-00	0.	0.8577E 00	0.8992E 00	0.9230E 00	0.9274E 00	1.0000E 00	0.1000E 01
0.4163E 03	0.1255E 04	0.	0.4277E 02	0.8090E 02	0.6863E 02	0.3753E 02	0.3726E 03	0.2893E 03
0.2262E 03	0.7076E 03	-0.	0.2472E 02	0.4938E 02	0.3655E 02	0.1922E 02	0.2025E 03	0.1572E 03
0.6763E-01	0.1273E-00	0.	0.1965E-00	0.2578E-00	0.3614E-00	0.4458E-00	0.6764E-01	0.6766E-01
0.2320E 01	0.2564E 01	-0.	0.2710E 01	0.2669E 01	0.2807E 01	0.3429E 01	0.2320E 01	0.2320E 01

(A) *Continued*

0.1000E 01	0.1000E 01	0.9513E 00	0.9563E 00	0.6715E 00	0.9067E 00	0.	0.4598E-00	0.4800E-00
0.2913E 03	0.3751E 03	0.4528E 02	0.9088E 02	0.8748E 02	0.5815E 02	0.	0.1415E 04	0.4191E 03
0.1712E 03	0.2204E 03	0.2830E 02	0.4850E 02	0.4627E 02	0.2708E 02	-0.	0.8046E 03	0.2463E 03
0.1527E-00	0.1527E-00	0.2494E-00	-0.1795E-00	0.2204E-00	-0.3738E-02	0.	0.8590E-01	0.1527E 01
0.2475E 01	0.2475E 01	0.2124E 01	0.2165E 01	0.2753E 01	0.2217E 01	-0.	0.2402E 01	0.2475E 01
0.1000E 01	1.0000E 00	0.9512E 00	0.9635E 00	0.9413E 00	0.8144E 00	0.	0.4645E-00	0.4503E-00
0.2715E 03	0.3496E 03	0.4680E 02	0.9158E 02	0.8089E 02	0.6214E 02	0.	0.1426E 04	0.3906E 03
0.1457E 03	0.1877E 03	0.2286E 02	0.4499E 02	0.4511E 02	0.3767E 02	-0.	0.7435E 03	0.2097E 03
0.2217E-00	0.2217E-00	0.5269E-01	0.4215E-01	0.2596E-00	0.2561E-00	-0.	0.2006E-00	0.2217E-00
0.2578E 01	0.2578E 01	0.2587E 01	0.2275E 01	0.2687E 01	0.2495E 01	-0.	0.2611E 01	0.2578E 01
1.0000E 00	1.0000E 00	0.9683E 00	0.9660E 00	0.9841E 00	0.9486E 00	0.	0.3011E-00	0.3339E-00
0.2899E 03	0.3733E 03	0.4987E 02	0.9730E 02	0.9090E 02	0.6948E 02	-0.	0.1624E 04	0.4171E 03
0.1498E 03	0.1929E 03	0.2067E 02	0.4184E 02	0.3515E 02	0.3348E 02	0.	0.7245E 03	0.2155E 03
0.9904E-01	0.9904E-01	-0.1225E-00	-0.8394E-01	-0.3153E-00	-0.6346E-01	-0.	-0.9330E-01	0.9904E-01
0.2732E 01	0.2732E 01	0.2786E 01	0.2902E 01	0.2856E 01	0.2530E 01	0.	0.2847E 01	0.2732E 01
0.1000E 01	0.1000E 01	0.9709E 00	0.9743E 00	0.9509E 00	0.8855E 00	-0.	0.3191E-01	-0.1331E-00
0.4741E 03	0.6106E 03	0.6946E 02	0.1327E 03	0.1359E 03	0.8976E 02	0.	0.2424E 04	0.6822E 03
0.1945E 03	0.2504E 03	0.1797E 02	0.3767E 02	0.4053E 02	0.2933E 02	-0.	0.9842E 03	0.2798E 03

(A) *Continued*

0.4116E-01	0.4116E-01	-0.2593E-00	0.1965E-00	0.2186E-00	0.1586E-01	0.	-0.8877E-01	0.4115E-01
0.2892E 01	0.2892E 01	0.2487E 01	0.2851E 01	0.3025E 01	0.2339E 01	-0.	0.2676E 01	0.2892E 01
0.1000E 01	1.0000E 01	0.9304E 00	0.9330E 00	0.8814E 00	0.7968E 00	0.	-0.1594E-00	-0.1071E-01
0.5052E 03	0.6505E 03	0.6634E 02	0.1297E 03	0.1245E 03	0.6817E 02	0.	0.2237E 04	0.7268E 03
0.1689E 03	0.2176E 03	0.2247E 02	0.4246E 02	0.4258E 02	0.2800E 02	-0.	0.6664E 03	0.2431E 03
-0.5386E-01	-0.5386E-01	-0.4081E-00	-0.4685E-00	-0.1610E-00	-0.2422E-00	0.	-0.4759E-00	-0.5386E-01
0.2617E 01	0.2617E 01	0.2915E 01	0.3369E 01	0.2523E 01	0.2400E 01	-0.	0.3021E 01	0.2617E 01
0.1000E 01	0.1000E 01	0.9548E 00	0.9558E 00	0.9548E 00	0.8800E 00	0.	0.3489E-00	-0.1658E-00
0.3672E 03	0.4728E 03	0.6412E 02	0.1197E 03	0.1047E 03	0.6034E 02	-0.	0.1714E 04	0.5283E 03
0.1892E 03	0.2437E 03	0.3268E 02	0.6233E 02	0.5675E 02	0.3589E 02	0.	0.8552E 03	0.2723E 03
-0.8895E-01	-0.8895E-01	-0.7920E-01	-0.1487E-00	-0.5326E-01	0.5633E-01	-0.	-0.1131E-00	-0.8895E-01
0.2267E 01	0.2267E 01	0.2106E 01	0.2266E 01	0.2291E 01	0.2350E 01	0.	0.2323E 01	0.2267E 01
1.0000E 00	1.0000E 00	0.9644E 00	0.9657E 00	0.9720E 00	0.9596E 00	0.	0.2284E-00	0.1332E-00
0.2199E 03	0.2832E 03	0.3745E 02	0.7044E 02	0.5973E 02	0.2828E 02	0.	0.1107E 04	0.3164E 03
0.1095E 03	0.1410E 03	0.1698E 02	0.3758E 02	0.2866E 02	0.1744E 02	-0.	0.5207E 03	0.1576E 03
0.3877E-00	0.3877E-00	0.2247E-00	0.4112E-00	0.2066E-01	0.3431E-00	0.	0.2497E-00	0.3877E-00

TABLE 3.1. (*continued*)

(B) Flood generation is summarized in the output, each flood event requiring two lines of data. In the first line, the month and type are provided. Month is numbered sequentially from 1 to the end of the simulation and the type indicates whether complete control is achieved; controlled floods are type 1, damaging floods are type 2. Unregulated and regulated flows routed to Walnutport and Bethlehem (in 10^2 acre ft/3 hr) are printed, followed by the calendar month (which varies cyclically from 1 to 12) of the flood and by the (originally) generated instantaneous peak flows at Walnutport and Bethlehem. In the second line the regulated and unregulated flows (10^2 acre ft/3 hr) at reservoirs 4, 5, and 6 are provided. All routed flows (10^2 acre ft/3 hr) are multiplied by a flood peak factor in the program to estimate instantaneous peaks.

STUDIES OF 50 YEARS STARTING WITH MONTH 1 CASE 5

MONTH	TYPE	WALNUTPORT		BETHLEHEM			GENERATED
28	2	0.6845E 02 / 0.	0.4399E 02 / 0.2644E 02	0.8345E 02 / 0.	0.5938E 02 / 0.3326E 01	4 / 0.8462E 02 / 0.	0.1058E 03 / 0.
51	2	0.9372E 02 / 0.	0.5931E 02 / 0.3682E 02	0.1145E 03 / 0.	0.8064E 02 / 0.4910E 01	3 / 0.1178E 03 / 0.	0.1473E 03 / 0.
60	1	0.5178E 02 / 0.	0.4356E 02 / 0.2036E 02	0.6142E 02 / 0.	0.5360E 02 / 0.2715E 01	12 / 0.6515E 02 / 0.	0.8144E 02 / 0.
179	2	0.7449E 02 / 0.	0.4767E 02 / 0.2870E 02	0.8841E 02 / 0.	0.6199E 02 / 0.3826E 01	11 / 0.9183E 02 / 0.	0.1148E 03 / 0.
264	1	0.5828E 02 / 0.	0.3228E 02 / 0.2343E 02	0.7036E 02 / 0.	0.4522E 02 / 0.6775E 01	12 / 0.7499E 02 / 0.	0.9373E 02 / 0.
335	1	0.4904E 02 / 0.	0.4131E 02 / 0.1895E 02	0.5990E 02 / 0.	0.5238E 02 / 0.4250E 01	11 / 0.6064E 02 / 0.	0.7580E 02 / 0.
352	2	0.7286E 02 / 0.	0.4665E 02 / 0.2804E 02	0.8920E 02 / 0.	0.6331E 02 / 0.3739E 01	4 / 0.8974E 02 / 0.	0.1122E 03 / 0.
373	1	0.4657E 02 / 0.	0.2983E 02 / 0.1792E 02	0.5644E 02 / 0.	0.3995E 02 / 0.2390E 01	1 / 0.5736E 02 / 0.	0.7170E 02 / 0.
385	2	0.5357E 02 / 0.	0.4395E 02 / 0.2076E 02	0.6486E 02 / 0.	0.5539E 02 / 0.2768E 01	1 / 0.6642E 02 / 0.	0.8303E 02 / 0.
387	1	0.5112E 02 / 0.	0.4275E 02 / 0.1970E 02	0.6257E 02 / 0.	0.5445E 02 / 0.2627E 01	3 / 0.6305E 02 / 0.	0.7882E 02 / 0.
411	1	0.5150E 02 / 0.	0.3068E 02 / 0.2267E 02	0.6315E 02 / 0.	0.4271E 02 / 0.2671E 01	3 / 0.6410E 02 / 0.	0.8013E 02 / 0.
416	2	0.7170E 02 / 0.	0.5615E 02 / 0.2775E 02	0.8620E 02 / 0.	0.7111E 02 / 0.3700E 01	8 / 0.8881E 02 / 0.	0.1110E 03 / 0.
459	1	0.6137E 02 / 0.	0.2715E 02 / 0.3891E 02	0.7499E 02 / 0.	0.4172E 02 / 0.3550E 01	3 / 0.7936E 02 / 0.	0.9920E 02 / 0.
476	1	0.5424E 02 / 0.	0.3476E 02 / 0.2089E 02	0.6611E 02 / 0.	0.4690E 02 / 0.2785E 01	8 / 0.6684E 02 / 0.	0.8355E 02 / 0.
536	1	0.4744E 02 / 0.	0.4038E 02 / 0.1828E 02	0.5788E 02 / 0.	0.5105E 02 / 0.3455E 01	8 / 0.5850E 02 / 0.	0.7313E 02 / 0.
567	1	0.5148E 02 / 0.	0.3317E 02 / 0.1994E 02	0.6266E 02 / 0.	0.4477E 02 / 0.2658E 01	3 / 0.6379E 02 / 0.	0.7974E 02 / 0.

TABLE 3.1. (*continued*)

(C) A portion of the array of design variables is printed as a matrix for identification. For each of the six reservoirs, monthly values are printed for the flood storage allowance (FSA), first and second recreation storage constraints (RECSTO and RECST2), and minimum flows (QMIN), all in 10^3 acre ft. Monthly values are also printed for the system target outputs for water supply (QTARG) in 10^3 acre ft, and for energy (ETARG) in megawatt hours.

INITIAL PRINT-OUT, DESIGN VARIABLES, RUN NO. 5

	JAN	FEB	MAR	APR	MAY	JUN	JUL	AUG	SEP	OCT	NOV	DEC
FSA(TAF)												
1	-0.	-0.	-0.	-0.	-0.	-0.	-0.	-0.	-0.	-0.	-0.	-0.
2	111.500	111.500	111.500	111.500	111.500	111.500	111.500	111.500	111.500	111.500	111.500	111.500
3	-0.	-0.	-0.	-0.	-0.	-0.	-0.	-0.	-0.	-0.	-0.	-0.
4	25.200	25.200	25.200	25.200	25.200	25.200	25.200	25.200	25.200	25.200	25.200	25.200
5	-0.	-0.	-0.	-0.	-0.	-0.	-0.	-0.	-0.	-0.	-0.	-0.
6	-0.	-0.	-0.	-0.	-0.	-0.	-0.	-0.	-0.	-0.	-0.	-0.
RECSTO(TAF)												
1	0.	0.	0.	0.	0.	0.	0.	0.	0.	0.	0.	0.
2	139.677	139.677	139.677	139.677	139.677	139.677	139.677	139.677	139.677	139.677	139.677	139.677
3	0.	0.	0.	0.	0.	0.	0.	0.	0.	0.	0.	0.
4	11.000	11.000	11.000	11.000	11.000	11.000	11.000	11.000	11.000	11.000	11.000	11.000
5	0.	0.	0.	0.	0.	0.	0.	0.	0.	0.	0.	0.
6	0.	0.	0.	0.	0.	0.	0.	0.	0.	0.	0.	0.
RECST2(TAF)												
1	0.	0.	0.	0.	0.	0.	0.	0.	0.	0.	0.	0.
2	36.666	36.666	36.666	36.666	36.666	36.666	36.666	36.666	36.666	36.666	36.666	36.666
3	11.000	11.000	11.000	11.000	11.000	11.000	11.000	11.700	11.000	11.000	11.000	11.000
4	0.	0.	0.	0.	0.	0.	0.	0.	0.	0.	0.	0.
5	0.	0.	0.	0.	0.	0.	0.	0.	0.	0.	0.	0.
QMIN(TAF)												
1	-0.	-0.	-0.	-0.	-0.	-0.	-0.	-0.	-0.	-0.	-0.	-0.
2	3.800	3.800	3.800	3.800	3.800	3.800	3.800	3.800	3.800	3.800	3.800	3.800
3	-0.	-0.	-0.	-0.	-0.	-0.	-0.	-0.	-0.	-0.	-0.	-0.
4	1.000	1.000	1.000	1.000	1.000	1.000	1.000	1.000	1.000	1.000	1.000	1.000
5	-0.	-0.	-0.	-0.	-0.	-0.	-0.	-0.	-0.	-0.	-0.	-0.
6	-0.	-0.	-0.	-0.	-0.	-0.	-0.	-0.	-0.	-0.	-0.	-0.
QTARG(TAF)	41.800	41.800	45.100	45.100	45.100	48.900	48.900	48.900	45.600	45.100	45.100	41.800

TABLE 5.1 (continued)

(D) Further elements from the set of design variables and their associated costs are tabulated. The abbreviations and units are:

PCAP — Power capacity, megawatts
PCPCST — Capital cost of powerplant, 10^3 dollars
PCPOMR — OMR cost of powerplant, 10^3 dollars
CAPACITY — Reservoir capacity, 10^3 acre ft.
DEAD — Dead storage capacity, 10^3 acre ft.
CAPCST — Capital cost, reservoir, 10^3 dollars
CAPOMR — OMR cost, reservoir, 10^3 dollars
RECCST — Capital cost, recreation facilities, 10^3 dollars
RECOMR — OMR cost, recreation facilities, 10^3 dollars
CAPDIV — Capacity, diversion channel to reservoir 3, 10^3 acre ft/month

RESERVOIR AND TURBINE NUMBER

	1	2	3	4	5	6	7	8	9
PCAP(MW)	-0.	-0.	-0.	10.0000	-0.	-0.	-0.	200.0000	-0.
PCPCST(THOUSANDS)	0.	0.	0.	0.	0.	0.	-0.	0.	0.
PCPOMR(THOUSANDS)	0.	0.	0.	65.3	0.	0.	0.	429.9	0.
CAPACITY(TAF)	0.	530.0000	-0.	120.0000	-0.	0.	0.	-0.	-0.
DEAD(TAF)	-0.	2.0000	-0.	11.0000	-0.	-0.	0.	0.	
CAPCST(THOUSANDS)	0.	0.	0.	0.	0.	0.			
CAPOMR(THOUSANDS)	0.	117.4	0.	84.1	0.	0.			
RECCST(THOUSANDS)	0.	0.	0.	0.	0.	0.			
RECOMR(THOUSANDS)	0.	181.8	0.	194.9	0.	0.			
CAPDIV(TAF/MON)			0.0020						

TABLE 3.1 (*continued*)

(E) The physical and economic consequences of simulating for the demand period are tabulated. For each reservoir, there appear the maximal and minimal contents (in 10^3 acre ft), the number of spills and emptyings, and the tidal analysis, giving the frequency with which the value of final contents of each reservoir lies in each of 10 deciles. A statistical summary of floods, energy, water supply and recreation deficits, and energy surplus is given. Tabulated values show average annual, maximal monthly and the number of events for each category. The 25 percent analysis shows the number of months for which the energy deficit (LOW) and energy surplus (HIGH) exceeds 25 percent of the energy target. Finally, summary economic data for the demand period appears in two rows. Row 1 shows mean values and row 2, standard deviations, all in 10^3 dollars.

(E)

THIS OUTPUT BLOCK COVERS THE PERIOD FROM YEAR 41 TO YEAR 90   RUN NUMBER 5

(SIMULATION PERIOD IS 600 MONTHS)

RES. NO	MAX CON TAF	MIN CON TAF	NO.OF FILLS	NO.OF EMPTY	STATIONARY STATE RESERVOIR VALUES									
					1	2	3	4	5	6	7	8	9	10
1	0.	0.	600	600	0	0	0	0	0	0	0	0	0	600
2	418.	110.	0	0	0	0	14	34	38	61	147	306	0	0
3	0.	0.	600	600	0	0	0	0	0	0	0	0	0	600
4	95.	21.	0	0	0	1	0	0	1	2	3	593	0	0
5	0.	0.	600	600	0	0	0	0	0	0	0	0	0	600
6	0.	0.	600	600	0	0	0	0	0	0	0	0	0	600

FLOODS		ENERGY DEFICITS				WS DEFICITS					REC. DEFICITS				ENERGY SURPLUS					25FC-ANAL.	
AV. NO. PER YR	MAX. PK. AT BETHLEHEM, THOU OF CFS	AV.ANN.	MAX	MON	NUM	AV.ANN.	MAX	MON	NUM	NUM	AV.ANN.	MAX	MON	NUM	AV.ANN.	MAX	MON	NUM	YRS	LOW	HIGH
	WITHOUT WITH	MWH				THOU.OF A-F			YRS		THOU.OF DOLLARS			YRS	MWH						
0.340	54.9781 38.7049	0.	0.	131.	0.	0.	0.	21.	0.	294.	40.	62766.	65794.	47.						0.	137.

	FLOOD BEN.	RECR. BEN.	W.S. BEN.	ENERGY BEN.	ANNUAL DAM		NON-FLOOD LESS DAMAGE	
					WITH	WITHOUT	WITH	WITHOUT

(ALL ENTRIES IN THOUSANDS)

0.183E 03	0.134E 04	0.354E 04	0.295E 04	0.592E 02	0.242E 03	0.778E 04	0.759E 04
0.363E 03	0.548E 02	0.171E 01	0.163E 03	0.178E 03	0.516E 03		

TABLE 3.1 (*continued*)

(F) A cumulative summary over the current and all preceding demand periods is tabulated at 10 levels of discount rate. The terminating status of the random number generator and final contents of the six reservoirs are provided so that subsequent analyses may be initiated using the terminal state of the system.

SUMMARY AND CUMULATION
(THOUSANDS OF DOLLARS)

DISCOUNT RATE	PV OF COSTS CAPITAL	OMR	ENERGY	WS	P V O F BENEFITS RECREATION	FLOOD	GROSS	NET
0.	0.120E 06	0.966E 05	0.267E 06	0.242E 06	0.121E 06	0.496E 05	0.680E 06	0.463E 06
2.00	0.120E 06	0.446E 05	0.124E 06	0.896E 05	0.562E 05	0.296E 05	0.299E 06	0.135E 06
2.50	0.120E 06	0.383E 05	0.107E 06	0.723E 05	0.482E 05	0.266E 05	0.254E 06	0.953E 05
3.00	0.120E 06	0.333E 05	0.928E 05	0.590E 05	0.419E 05	0.241E 05	0.218E 06	0.644E 05
3.50	0.120E 06	0.293E 05	0.817E 05	0.489E 05	0.369E 05	0.219E 05	0.189E 06	0.400E 05
4.00	0.120E 06	0.260E 05	0.728E 05	0.409E 05	0.328E 05	0.200E 05	0.167E 06	0.204E 05
4.50	0.120E 06	0.234E 05	0.655E 05	0.346E 05	0.295E 05	0.184E 05	0.148E 06	0.450E 04
5.00	0.120E 06	0.212E 05	0.594E 05	0.297E 05	0.267E 05	0.169E 05	0.133E 06	-0.855E 04
5.50	0.120E 06	0.194E 05	0.543E 05	0.256E 05	0.244E 05	0.157E 05	0.120E 06	-0.194E 06
6.00	0.120E 06	0.178E 05	0.500E 05	0.224E 05	0.225E 05	0.146E 05	0.109E 06	-0.285E 05

RUN   5   R1=266375567215

| FINAL STORAGES | -0. | | 0.3157E 04 | -0. | 0.9480E 03 | -0. | | -0. |

Subroutine RANDM

There are several sequences in the program which require a random number. For example, the operational hydrology generator, the flood peak generator, the selection of a time of peak, and the division of the flood duration between rising and falling limbs require either normally distributed or rectangularly distributed random numbers. Subroutine RANDM provides rectangularly distributed random numbers in the range, 0–1. If normally distributed deviates are required, the transforms

$$S_j = [-2 \ln R_j]^{1/2} \cos(2\pi R_{j+1})$$
$$S_{j+1} = [-2 \ln R_j]^{1/2} \sin(2\pi R_{j+1})$$

are applied to successive pairs of rectangular random numbers (R_j, R_{j+1}) to produce pairs of standard deviates (S_j, S_{j+1}). These deviates can be further modified by adjusting their skewness to accommodate the case of gamma-inflow distributions; this is done in Subroutine SYNHYD.

At the end of every run the current status of the random-number generator is printed in octal mode so that subsequent runs can be made using identical random numbers. That is, the random-number generator can be initiated with a particular starting index which assures that all subsequently generated numbers conform to some pattern. Thus it is appropriate to distinguish our random numbers by the prefix "pseudo" because, given a starting key, the numbers are not random at all but, in fact, describe a deterministic sequence. However, they retain all the prerequisites of a random sequence, and if the starting key is chosen at random the resulting sequence is adequate for purposes of this model.

4 VALIDATION AND APPLICATION OF THE PROGRAM

VALIDATION

Having devised the necessary technological and economic functions, having settled upon a strategy for operating the system, and having written the machine code, we must run the program to assure its validity. This assurance rests on whether the program is free of:

   (i) blunders and program bugs,
  (ii) internal inconsistencies, and
 (iii) discrepancies between generated values and their presumed (external) distributions.

The Presence of Blunders

The difference between a program bug and a blunder is merely one of subtlety. For example, if a key-punching error (in data or program cards) or a logical error produces negative reservoir contents or some other absurd result, the programmer should search for a blunder in the code or input data. If the problem is more subtle, requiring greater imagination (and perhaps intermediate output and memory dumps) to unearth, the programmer hunts for a bug. Operationally the result is the same—further running ceases until the error is flushed out of the input deck.

While those subroutines rendering few decisions (e.g., READ1, READ2, POWER, BENDYN) were happily free of subtle bugs, the Monthly and Flood Algorithm subroutines taxed our debugging skill. Only the liberal use of intermediate print-out, obtained via console option, enabled us to converge on perfect agreement between programmed and manual computations. Particularly troublesome were the EXECUTIVE Routine and Subroutines ROUTER, SPACE, and SUPPOW, which together accounted for perhaps 75 percent of the total debugging and testing time.

Internal Inconsistencies

In the Lehigh program there are few opportunities for internal inconsistency. The physical processes simulated by the program deal with continuity, flood routing, and with generation of hydroelectric energy; the ensuing algebraic relationships are well established in engineering practice and can be symbolized reliably by simple analytic formulations. If the model necessitated estimates of flows or flow components represented by complicated, approximate functions, such as ground-water movement and seepage losses through dam embankments, the reliability of the simulation would be subject to more rigorous examination. Even if the physical laws governing these flows were perfectly known, the problem of collecting and summarizing the required data would be formidable. However, to further compound the problem, these laws and even the choice of independent variables with which to express them, are imperfectly known. In these instances a useful technique is to express the relationships in stochastic or probabilistic form; this requires estimation of the statistical parameters of the observed phenomena.

One criterion of internal consistency, then, is that all the relevant flow vectors be appropriately described in either deterministic or stochastic mode, and that the numerical results which obtain from such descriptions be consistent with the statistical properties of the observations.

The characteristic time-interval for the model must be chosen with care. Suppose a reservoir has shallow slopes; a small change in its contents might induce a large change in reservoir surface area. Consequently, an estimate of, say, the monthly evaporation loss, if based on initial storage, may be substantially in error; it might be necessary to correct the estimate by utilizing as the basis of the evaporation calculation some intermediate storage value, computed from both the initial and final monthly contents. In the Lehigh program this technique appears in the algorithm for computing hydroelectric energy (Subroutine POWER), where initial and final contents are averaged and define an intermediate head on which the energy computation is based. Alternatively, the time-interval, here taken as one month, could be shortened such that the initial state of the system suffices to evaluate the output and hence the response. In many models it would be appropriate to utilize several time-intervals; the Lehigh study is based on a monthly simulation, but for analysis of floods it considers 3-hour intervals. Further refinements, such as analysis of diurnal fluctuations of power output, could be included.

Consistency of Generated and Observed Hydrologic Values

The Lehigh simulation program generates two sets of operational hydrology inputs — monthly and flood flows. It is essential that the hydrology generators preserve the relevant moments and covariances of the observed variables. Some compromise with reality might be necessary if one or another of the historical sequences does not appear to be derived from a standard statistical distribution. In this case some combination (or convolution) of distributions may be employed; more generally, the observations are presumed to obtain from a standard distribution and the discrepancies between observed and generated distributions, if not potentially damaging, are ignored. It is clear that attainment of, or proximity to, statistical consistency (or indistinguishability) between generated values and the observations is necessary if the model is to be judged reliable. This requirement applies equally to the validation of other vectors of the model as well as to the input hydrology.

Necessity and Sufficiency

In mathematical terms, the conditions stipulated in the preceding paragraphs are necessary but not sufficient for accepting the simulation model. If one or more criteria are substantively violated, the model or the associated program (or both) is invalid; if no criterion is violated, the ultimate acceptability of the model is likely, but further testing is indicated. For example, historical flows should be provided as inputs to the simulation model so that the model's response can be compared to that obtained by traditional analyses (for example, by system operating studies which encompass the "critical period" of the record).

Acceptance of the Streamflow Generator

In earlier studies of the application of operational hydrology to system design[1] the details of the synthetic flow traces and their

[1] A. Maass, M. Hufschmidt, R. Dorfman, H. Thomas, S. Marglin and G. Fair, *Design of water-resource systems* (Harvard University Press, Cambridge, 1962).

statistical parameters were presented; to augment the theoretical discussion these were shown to compare favorably with their historical counterparts. No such demonstration is offered in this book because continued experience with generating models of the sort described in Chapter 2 confirms the reliability of the technique and because, ultimately, the validity of the generating scheme should not be measured solely by the acceptability of the generated hydrologic output. This last point merits amplification because it is a departure from traditional practice.

If the streamflow data at all sites are arrayed and plotted, the covariance matrix can be deduced. If the moments of these several records are consistent with a multivariate normal parent distribution at the usual levels of significance, it remains only to investigate the time-dependence among the principal components of the records. That is, being satisfied that the data might be samples derived from a multivariate normal population, the next step is to determine whether that population is Markovian (characterized by a single serial correlation coefficient at each site) or subsumed under some other structure. Sophisticated mathematical analysis is ordinarily required to decide this question. Examination of correlograms, periodograms, spectral densities, and other functional forms derived from the covariance matrix helps to establish the structure of the model; but even with all of these techniques, no clear discriminating rule need necessarily emerge. For the Lehigh study it was determined that the data derive from a multivariate normal population characterized by an underlying Markov process. That is, the first serial correlation coefficient and the covariance matrix suffice to define all the relevant properties of the parent distribution; use of the lag one generating model as described in Chapter 2 is predicated on this finding.[2]

If the historical data cannot be ascribed to a multivariate normal population, suitably chosen transforms might remedy the matter. The usual transforms are log and square root but if they do not help, the regression equations between sites, and particularly the form of the additive standard errors of estimate, must either be cast in terms of some tractable function or abandoned. Finally, if the generating process does not appear to be Markovian, higher-order

[2] When the study was extended to the Delaware basin, it appeared better to generate operational hydrology from a log-normal parent distribution.

serial correlation coefficients must be included in the scheme for synthesizing flows. Testing the significance of these higher order coefficients is not a trivial task, but the statistical literature contains several appropriate citations.[3]

The mathematical model can now be presumed to represent the hydrologic regime because spatial and temporal requirements (i.e., moment and covariance maintenance) are satisfied. If the co-efficients so derived are used to produce synthetic flows, there would appear to be no reason for inconsistency between historical and generated values. To guard against programming or computational error, it is advisable to calculate the first few moments of the generated flows and to compare them to their observed counterparts. Deviations which cannot be explained by sampling instability can be traced to faulty data-processing or to erroneous acceptance of the model. That is, if the data derive from a parent gamma-distribution while a normal generating model is postulated, divergent results will be obtained and these must be rectified, accepted, or, however reluctantly, discarded completely.

Negative flows might be generated from time to time in models not characterized by logarithmic transformations. Streams with small flows are particularly susceptible to this phenomenon, and experience dictates that setting these values to zero introduces a small but insignificant bias into the results;[4] consequently, this procedure is recommended.

Measures of Risk Aversion

In the Lehigh simulation study we attempt to maximize the present value of expected net benefits, and specifically disregard all other moments of the output distribution. Thus our technique would be indifferent between two designs which generate identical expected returns. But higher moments of that output distribution associated with any design can be readily evaluated by simulation, and since output variability is generally regarded as undesirable, a design with a small second moment (or standard deviation) would be preferred to some other design with an equal expected return

[3] See, for example, M. G. Kendall and A. Stuart, *The advanced theory of statistics* (Hafner, New York, 1961), vol. II, chaps. 25–30.
[4] Maass, Hufschmidt, *et al.*, chap. 12, reference 1.

but a large second moment. The Lehigh program calculates the first moments of the benefit distribution ascribed to each design, and in the event of a tie in ranking the alternatives, the second moment may be invoked to discriminate between schemes.

Additional moments are required to describe the benefits more completely unless their distribution is known to be normal. In general, no such assurance can be made but the influence of the third and higher moments on the ranking function is apt to be small; consequently, most analyses are confined to a consideration of mean and standard deviation only.

A large variance (of the benefit distribution) commonly implies an uncertain outcome; thus variance can be construed to measure the riskiness of a design. In some studies it might be possible to blend the mean and standard deviation of benefits, and attempt to maximize the linear combination, $\mu + a\sigma$, where μ is the expected benefit, σ is the standard deviation of benefits, and a is a parameter which reflects the planner's aversion to risk. Ordinarily, a is negative so that high-output variability, manifested by a large value of σ, penalizes the objective function more than low-output variability. For gamblers, a is positive; it is the very uncertainty of the outcome which makes a gamble attractive. For conservative planners, the magnitude of a is large; for them, the ranking function ascribed to a given alternative decreases sharply (though linearly) with σ.

Maximization of the function $\mu + a\sigma$ is tantamount to selecting that investment which maximizes expected return consistent with a given level of risk aversion. This ranking function might be generally applied to design of water-resource systems, whereupon the standard deviation of system performance is invoked not only when ranking two or more alternatives with equal expected returns but when ranking all design alternatives. It is conceivable that the optimal design would have a lower expected return than several of its competitors, but if this were so it would necessarily provide a more stable output than these same competitors. In the Lehigh study we rank designs on expectation only; it is strongly urged that subsequent studies consider the possibilities of evaluating a parameter of risk aversion and of incorporating the additive term $a \cdot \sigma$ in the objective function.

APPLICATION OF THE MODEL

Upon validation, the model is ready for application to the problem of optimal system design. In general, the approach is to select a sampling strategy whereby the domain of possible designs can be sampled and better designs can be identified by an explicit procedure until no further improvement in net benefits is obtained. The detailed application of such a strategy is presented elsewhere[5] and is not illustrated here.

Our application of the Lehigh simulation program had a more modest goal. We set out to investigate the feasibility of using simulation to test alternative designs for a system characterized by 42 major design variables and a dynamic investment pattern. From the investigations we hoped (1) to gain information on the advantages and disadvantages of applying simulation to a design problem of this degree of complexity, and (2) to devise criteria and rules for undertaking subsequent analyses of this type. A derived goal was to study random sampling techniques in problems characterized by an unmanageably large number of design alternatives or permutations.

Strategy

1. A random sample of 20 designs was constructed as follows:

(a) The Case number (1 through 5) was selected at random for each design. This choice dictated selection of reservoir 1 or 2 and power plant 1, 2, 7, 8, or 9.

(b) The range of storage capacity for each reservoir (i.e., from 0 to the maximum value) was divided into 10 equal segments, and a design value was selected at random from the set of 10 values for each reservoir (zero value being inadmissible).

(c) Five demand periods were assumed; at the start of each period, one or more reservoirs could be added to the system if desired. Reservoirs were assigned to demand periods by a special random sampling procedure which assigned higher probabilities to selection in early demand periods than in later periods, and which provided for zero-reservoir designs by allowing assignment of a reservoir to an imaginary demand period.

[5] Maass, Hufschmidt, *et al.*, chap. 10, reference 1, and M. Hufschmidt, "Simulating the behavoir of a multi-unit, multi-purpose water-resource system," in A. C. Hoggatt and F. E. Balderston, *Symposium on simulation models: methodology and applications to the behavioral sciences* (South-Western Publishing Co., Cincinnati, 1963).

(d) A total flood-storage allowance for the system was selected at random from a range of system flood storages, and apportioned to individual reservoirs according to predetermined ratios proportional to the drainage areas above the several reservoirs.

(e) Other major design variables — target water-supply output, target energy output, power plant capacities, dead-storage allocations, and the two recreation constraint levels — were selected at random from ranges of the variables; these ranges were increasingly constrained as additional design variables were selected, thereby reducing the likelihood of selecting designs for which the decision variables were grossly mismatched.

The length of each of the demand periods 1–4 was set at 10 years, and that of the fifth demand period, at 50 years; the period of economic analysis (being the sum of the five demand periods) was 90 years. For each demand period the performance of the system was simulated for 50 years, so that each system design (comprising 5 demand periods) was tested for 250 years (3000 months) of simulated operation.

2. The three best designs — those with the highest net benefits — were subjected to systematic, sequential analysis using the single-factor and marginal analysis methods.[6] Analysis of the results of each design change led to further changes in values of design variables and to simulation runs using these new designs. This sequential process was continued until no further significant improvement was obtained. As in the random sampling phase, each system design encompassed five demand periods, simulation was performed for 250 years, and synthetic traces of hydrology were used.

3. The final step was the testing of the best design using both synthetic traces and recorded flows, and under the two alternative methods for discounting annual benefits.

Results

From the random sample. As expected, the net benefits obtained from the random sample of 20 designs varied widely. As shown in Table 4.1, the range in net benefits (adjusted to exclude flood control benefits obtained from the existing Bear Creek Reservoir) was

[6] Maass, Hufschmidt, *et al.*, pp. 395–398, reference 1.

TABLE 4.1. Summary of costs and benefits; random sample of 20 designs.

Design	Case	Cost (10⁶ dollars)		Benefits[a] (10⁶ dollars)					Net	
		Capital	OMR	Energy	Water Supply	Recrea-tion	Flood Control	Gross	Un-adjusted	Adjusted[b]
1	3	113.0	33.5	15.5	28.2	53.3	34.1	131.0	−15.3	−36.6
2	4	141.0	41.1	51.7	43.6	58.2	29.6	183.0	1.4	−19.9
3	4	65.4	19.8	11.5	11.7	22.9	30.6	76.7	−8.5	−29.8
4	3	95.8	30.8	17.9	13.9	50.3	31.3	113.0	−13.3	−34.6
5	5	71.6	22.6	38.9	31.5	43.7	30.5	109.3	15.1	−6.2
6	5	110.7	28.9	14.4	62.3	41.5	27.7	146.3	6.7	−14.6
7	2	161.0	52.8	67.6	33.8	72.6	26.0	200.0	−14.3	−35.6
8	2	180.0	54.3	72.7	34.7	81.1	27.0	215.5	−0.5	−21.8
9	3	122.0	38.7	31.5	21.3	50.1	29.0	131.9	−28.8	−50.1
10	1	95.1	29.9	10.7	47.9	45.5	22.7	127.0	1.4	−19.9
11	2	192.0	59.1	82.9	43.5	95.0	25.9	247.3	−3.8	−25.1
12	1	96.0	34.4	12.4	13.6	58.8	25.2	110.6	−21.8	−43.1
13	3	30.6	9.4	4.1	15.7	14.8	26.5	61.1	21.1	−0.2
14	5	100.0	22.6	30.8	14.4	25.4	27.7	98.3	−24.6	−45.9
15	4	142.0	30.6	40.3	14.4	61.1	30.8	146.6	−26.0	−47.3
16	5	160.0	46.7	94.3	57.9	56.3	32.9	241.0	34.3	13.0
17	3	55.0	16.8	5.9	−37.7	26.3	29.0	23.5	−48.3	−69.6
18	3	43.6	10.9	1.4	40.6	16.7	27.8	86.5	32.0	10.7
19	3	60.8	15.9	0.0	30.6	20.3	29.4	80.3	3.6	−17.7
20	2	147.0	48.6	74.7	63.7	77.8	25.9	242.0	46.4	25.1[c]

[a] Present value of annual benefits over 90 years at 2½ percent discount rate.
[b] Adjustment consists of subtracting 21.3×10^6 dollars of flood control benefits obtained from existing Bear Creek reservoir.

from −$69.6 million (design 17) to +$25.1 million (design 20). (In design 17 the chosen recreation constraint levels generated huge water-supply deficits, thus depressing water-supply benefits to −$37.7 million.) The median value was −$21 million and the mean was −$23.5 million.

Only three designs showed positive net benefits. The best design (no. 20) involved (a) large capital investment ($147 million), which included construction of five reservoirs (1 and 3 through 6) plus the high-head power development from reservoir 1, and (b) high target levels of energy and water supply. The second-best design (no. 16), also capital intensive ($160 million), included 5 reservoirs (2–6) and involved high energy and water-supply targets. In contrast, the third-ranking design (no. 18) had a relatively low capital cost ($43.6 million), only three reservoirs (3–5) and an extremely low energy target.

From the sequential analysis. The three best designs provided the starting points for sequential analysis. With design 16 as the base (adjusted net benefits of $13 million), successive changes in design variables were made as shown in Table 4.2. Eliminating reservoir 3 and setting the water-supply target to the highest level consistent with the demand assumptions for water supply resulted in a substantial increase of $34.3 million in adjusted net benefits to a level of $47.3 million. However, simulation of this design over 3000 months generated 29 monthly energy deficits greater than 25 percent of the monthly energy target. To eliminate or reduce these intolerable deficits, construction of reservoir 2 was advanced from the second to the first demand period while construction of reservoir 5 was delayed from the first to the second demand period. Net benefits increased by $9 million and the number of intolerable deficits fell to 10. Reduction of the energy target and associated power plant size by 10 percent eliminated the intolerable deficits and raised net benefits by $2 million. A necessary design correction shifted construction of reservoir 4 to the first demand period because it serves as an afterbay to the high-head power plant at reservoir 1; this change reduced net benefits only slightly. Finally, analysis of the simulation results of this design suggested the elimination of reservoirs 5 and 6. This change proved to be profitable, as net benefits rose by $17.2 million. Approximately $35 million in capital and OMR costs were saved, and,

TABLE 4.2. Summary of costs and benefits, systematic sample of eight designs, using design no. 16 of random sample as the base.

| Design | Changes in design variable | Costs (10⁶ dollars) | | | Benefits[a] (10⁶ dollars) | | | | | | | No. of intolerable energy deficits[c] |
		Capital	OMR	Energy	Water supply	Recreation	Flood control	Gross	Net Unadjusted	Net Adjusted[b]	Change from base design	
1	Base design (no. 16, Table 4.1)	160	46.7	94.3	57.9	56.3	32.9	241	34.3	13.0	—	18
2	Reservoir 3 eliminated	133	40.5	87.1	57.9	49.1	32.0	226	52.5	31.2	+18.2	104
3	Water supply output increased to top values	160	46.7	94.3	72.3	56.0	33.3	256	49.3	28.0	+15.0	20
4	Recreation constraint levels set to vary over months	160	46.7	94.5	57.9	54.1	33.3	240	33.3	12.0	−1.0	10
5	Reservoir 3 eliminated and water supply target set at top values	130	40.4	84.0	72.3	51.0	31.8	239	68.6	47.3	+34.3	29
6	With design 5 as new base, construction of reservoir 2 advanced from second to first demand period; reservoir 5 delayed from first to second demand period	146	46.4	112.0	72.3	53.9	31.4	270	77.6	56.3	+9.0	10
7	With design 6 as new base, energy target reduced by 10 percent; power plant capacity reduced from 225 mw to 200 mw	142	42.7	106.0	72.3	55.2	31.2	264	79.8	58.3	+2.0	0
8	With design 7 as new base, reservoir 4 advanced from second to first demand period	148	45.8	106.0	72.3	61.4	31.5	272	78.1	56.8	−1.5	0
9	With design 8 as new base, reservoirs 5 and 6 eliminated	120	38.3	107.0	72.3	48.2	26.6	254	95.3	74.0	+17.2	0

[a] Present value of annual benefits over 90 years at 2½ percent discount rate.
[b] Adjustment consists of subtracting 21.3 × 10⁶ dollars of flood control benefits obtained from existing Bear Creek reservoir.
[c] In 3000 months of simulation.

while recreation and flood control benefits fell by about $18 million, energy and water-supply benefits were substantially unaffected by the change. The analysis of this design terminated at this point, with capital and OMR costs at $158.3 million, gross benefits, $254 million, adjusted net benefits, $74.0 million, and the benefit-cost ratio equal to 1.47. There were no intolerable energy deficits in 3000 months of simulation.

Sequential analysis of design 20 of the random sample (adjusted net benefits, $25.1 million) proceeded in like manner, as shown in Table 4.3. In the first variant from the base design, the energy target was reduced by 10 percent and the power plant capacity by 15 mw. This increased net benefits by $6.2 million and decreased the number of intolerable energy deficits from 270 in the base design to 100 in the revised design. Using the new design as a base, the second recreation constraint level at reservoir 1 was lowered (in effect, providing more available water for energy and water supply), and reservoir 3 was eliminated. The result was a substantial rise in net benefits (12.7 million) and a reduction of intolerable energy deficits to 68. The next iteration started with this design and strove to achieve a gain in net benefits and a reduction in number of intolerable energy deficits by making the following changes:

(1) reduction of target output for energy and of power plant capacity by 10 percent;

(2) increase of target output for water supply to maximum permissible values dictated by demand assumptions;

(3) increase of capacity of reservoir 1 from 341,500 to 400,000 acre ft;

(4) increase of flood storage allowance of reservoir 1 from 90,500 to 106,000 acre ft; and

(5) elimination of reservoirs 5 and 6 from the design.

The results were again favorable; net benefits were increased by $18.4 million and the number of intolerable energy deficits lowered to 14. No such deficits occurred in the first two demand periods because water supply targets were lower than for the last three demand periods. In an effort to eliminate these deficits, the target energy outputs were reduced by 10 percent in the last three demand periods; a test of this design produced only three such deficits

TABLE 4.3. Systematic sample of four designs, using design no. 20 of random sample as the base.

Design	Changes in design variable	Costs (10^6 dollars)			Benefits[a] (10^6 dollars)						Change from base design[b]	No. of intolerable energy deficits[c]
		Capital	OMR	Energy	Water supply	Recrea-tion	Flood control	Gross	Net Unadjusted	Net Adjusted[b]		
1	Base design (no. 20, Table 4.1)	147	48.6	74.7	63.7	77.8	25.9	242	46.4	25.1		270
2	Energy target reduced by 10 percent and power plant capacity reduced from 175 mw to 160 mw	145	47.2	74.3	63.9	80.7	25.7	245	52.6	31.3	+6.2	100
3	With design 2 as new base, reservoir 3 eliminated and second recreation constraint level reduced at reservoir 1	128	44.3	75.2	63.8	73.6	25.3	238	65.3	44.0	+12.7	68
4	With design 3 as new base, energy target and power plant capacity reduced by 10 percent, water supply target increased to its maximum permissible value, capacity of reservoir 1 increased by 58,500 acre ft, flood storage allowance of reservoir 1 increased by 15,500 acre ft, and reservoirs 5 and 6 eliminated	112	37.9	72.0	73.1	65.9	22.6	234	83.7	62.4	+18.4	14
5	With design 4 as new base, energy target reduced for demand periods 3, 4 and 5 by 10 percent	112	37.9	69.8	73.4	67.0	22.3	233	82.6	61.3	-1.1	3

[a] Present value of annual benefits over 90 years at 2½ percent discount rate.
[b] Adjustment consists of subtracting 21.3×10^6 dollars of flood control benefits obtained from existing Bear Creek reservoir.
[c] In 3000 months of simulation.

with but a slight decrease ($1.1 million) in net benefits, whereupon the analysis was terminated. Capital and OMR costs were about $150 million, gross benefits, $233 million, adjusted net benefits, $61.3 million, and the benefit-cost ratio was 1.4.

A sequential analysis, carried out for design 18 of the random sample (adjusted net benefits of $10.7 million), is summarized in Table 4.4. In the first variant, reservoir 3, power plant 3, and the energy target were deleted from the design with compensating increases in capacities of reservoirs 5 and 6. Recreation constraint levels at the two reservoirs were also raised. These changes yielded an increase of $11.9 million in net benefits. Using this design as the base, the water-supply target was increased to its maximum permissible value, and the two recreation constraint levels were reduced to provide more active long-term storage. The results, again favorable, showed a further gain of $22.7 million in net benefits. In the final design, the previous design provided the base; the completion dates for reservoirs 4 and 5 were reversed, with reservoir 5 construction delayed from the first to the fourth demand period, and reservoir 4 construction advanced from the fourth to the first period. The gain in net benefits was $6.4 million; this final design had capital and OMR costs of $57.3 million, gross benefits of $123.0 million, adjusted net benefits of $51.7 million, and a benefit-cost ratio of 1.8.

Sensitivity analysis. A few simulation runs were made of the best design obtained from sequential analysis (no. 9, Table 4.2) to examine the influence of hydrologic variations and changes in methods of discounting.

First, the design was run with a different trace of synthetic hydrology. As shown in Table 4.5, flood damages and flood-control benefits revealed the greatest sensitivity of all benefit sources to variations among the hydrologic inputs. For example, use of the base design with the initial synthetic trace produced a range of average annual flood-control benefits from $180,000 in demand period 5 to $1.34 million in demand period 4, and accounted for $26.6 million in present value of total flood-control benefits over the entire 90-year period of economic analysis. The same design run with a different trace of synthetic streamflows showed a range of average annual flood-control benefits from $250,000 in demand period 3 to $970,000 in demand period 1, and yielded $23.8 million

TABLE 4.4. Systematic sample of three designs, using design no. 18 of random sample as the base.

Design	Changes in design variable	Costs (10⁶ dollars)			Benefits[a] (10⁶ dollars)				Net		Change from base design
		Capital	OMR	Energy	Water supply	Recreation	Flood control	Gross	Unadjusted	Adjusted[b]	
1	Base design (no. 18, Table 4.1)	43.6	10.9	1.4	40.6	16.7	27.8	86.5	32.0	10.7	
2	Reservoir 3, power plant 3 and energy target eliminated; total capacity and first and second recreation constraint levels at reservoirs 4 and 5 increased	37.0	10.1	0	44.0	19.1	27.8	91.0	43.9	22.6	+11.9
3	With design 2 as new base, water supply target increased to its maximum permissible value, and first and second recreation constraint levels reduced at reservoirs 4 and 5	37.0	10.1	0	66.9	19.0	27.8	114.0	66.6	45.3	+22.7
4	With design 3 as a base, construction of reservoir 5 delayed from first to fourth demand period, and reservoir 4 advanced from fourth to first demand period	37.4	12.9	0	67.0	29.6	26.7	73.0	51.7		+6.4

[a] Present value of annual benefits over 90 years at 2½ percent discount rate.
[b] Adjustment consists of subtracting 21.3 × 10⁶ dollars of flood control benefits obtained from existing Bear Creek reservoir.

TABLE 4.5. Benefits and flood damages (in 10^6 dollars) for five demand periods and entire period of economic analysis for the base design (no. 9, Table 4.2) with three different hydrologic traces.

	Demand period					Entire period of economic analysis
	1	2	3	4	5	
1. Basic synthetic trace						
Benefits[a]						
Energy	3.06	3.02	2.95	2.94	2.95	107.0
Water supply	0.60	1.13	1.82	2.92	3.54	72.3
Recreation	1.36	1.36	1.34	1.35	1.34	48.2
Flood control	0.82	1.23	0.65	1.34	0.18	26.6
Flood damages[a]						
With	0.28	0.30	0.65	0.96	0.06	—
Without	1.10	1.54	1.30	2.30	0.24	—
Gross benefits[a]						254.0
Net benefits[a]						95.3
2. New synthetic trace						
Benefits[a]						
Energy	3.01	2.96	2.98	3.00	2.96	106.0
Water supply	0.60	1.13	1.82	2.92	3.54	72.3
Recreation	1.36	1.35	1.35	1.36	1.31	47.9
Flood control	0.97	0.55	0.25	0.73	0.67	23.8
Flood damages[a]						
With	0.66	0.60	0.12	0.55	0.36	—
Without	1.64	1.15	0.37	1.28	1.03	—
Gross benefits[a]						250.0
Net benefits[a]						91.8
3. Trace of actual record						
Benefits[a]						
Energy	2.90	2.87	2.98	2.89	2.91	104.0
Water supply	0.60	1.13	1.82	2.92	3.54	72.3
Recreation	1.31	1.36	1.34	1.35	1.33	47.5
Flood control	0	1.17	0.03	1.14	0.60	19.2
Flood damages[a]						
With	0	0.76	0.03	0.29	0.32	—
Without	0	1.93	0.06	1.43	0.92	—
Gross benefits[a]						243.0
Net benefits[a]						84.3

[a] Values are in 10^6 dollars and are average annual for each of demand periods 1–5; and present value with discount rate of $2\frac{1}{2}$ percent for entire period of economic analysis. Gross and net benefits include flood control benefits from existing Bear Creek reservoir.

in present value of total flood-control benefits. When the same design was run for a 90-year simulation with the actual record of streamflows (37 years, repeated as required to provide flows for the 90 years of simulation), average annual flood-control benefits ranged from zero in demand period 1 to $1.17 million in demand period 2, and the present value of total flood-control benefits was $19.2 million, somewhat lower than the equivalent values for the two runs with synthetic traces. Flood-control benefits were zero in the first 10-year demand period (which is also the first 10 years of the simulation) because there were no damaging floods in the first 10 years of the historic record. Similarly, the high flood-control benefits in the second and fourth demand periods of the run with historic streamflows are associated with the major floods of May 1942 and August 1955 in the Lehigh basin.

In contrast to flood-control benefits, the benefits for other purposes displayed only modest variations with alternate hydrology. For example, total present value of energy benefits ranged narrowly from $107 million for the base-design run with synthetic streamflows to $104 million for historic streamflows. The present value of gross water-supply benefits ($72.3 million) did not vary at all as hydrologic traces changed; this stability in benefits was achieved because the water-supply target is met in every month of simulation for all hydrologic traces, and, in the absence of water-supply deficits, gross benefits remain constant over all hydrologies.

The best design was next run under the two alternative methods of discounting annual benefits. As described in Chapter 2, in an *undiscounted run*, annual benefits are averaged for the entire demand period, and then discounted to the present, while, in a *discounted run*, benefits are discounted to the present from their year of occurrence. The random occurrence of flood damages (and hence flood-control benefits) and energy, water-supply and recreation deficits during the simulation gives rise to uneven time streams of benefits; in general, therefore, we expect differences to arise in the present value of benefits under the two methods of discounting. Such differences did arise, as shown in Table 4.6, which portrays the results of simulation runs of the base design with synthetic and actual hydrology traces each under the two methods of discounting. For both traces of hydrology, energy benefits were substantially less under the discounted run than under the un-

TABLE 4.6. Benefits for the base design, undiscounted and discounted simulation runs; for synthetic trace and trace of actual hydrology.

	Undiscounted run	Discounted run
1. Synthetic trace		
Benefits (10^6 dollars)[a]		
Energy	106.0	94.1
Water supply	72.3	72.3
Recreation	47.8	47.5
Flood control	13.3	13.2
Gross	239.0	227.0
Net	80.7	68.7
2. Actual hydrology trace		
Benefits (10^6 dollars)[a]		
Energy	104.0	92.7
Water supply	72.3	72.3
Recreation	47.5	47.5
Flood control	19.2	18.8
Gross	243.0	231.0
Net	84.3	72.9

[a] Present value over 90 years at discount rate of $2\frac{1}{2}$ percent. Net benefits include flood control benefits from existing Bear Creek reservoir.

discounted run. Other benefits, including (surprisingly) flood control, were quite insensitive to mode of discounting.

Comparison with the Corps design. As a final test, the Corps of Engineers design for the Lehigh system was simulated using the same synthetic hydrologic regime as for the random and systematic sample designs discussed earlier. The schedule of installation of the four reservoirs in the Corps plan called for demand periods of 7, 9, 8, 16, and 50 years, the last demand period covering 50 years after installation of the last reservoir. The Corps plan called for installation of reservoirs 4, 5, 6, and 2 in that order and for provision of water supply, flood control and recreation. No hydro power was included. The present value, at $2\frac{1}{2}$ percent discount rate, of capital and OMR costs was $63.2 million, gross benefits (exclusive of flood control benefits from existing Bear Creek reservoir) were $107.7 million, net benefits $44.2 million, and the benefit–cost ratio was 1.7. On a comparable basis, the three best designs obtained from our analyses had net benefits of $74 million, $61.3 million, and $51.7 million, and benefit–cost ratios of 1.47, 1.4, and 1.8. Of significance is the fact that with simulation runs of only 35 trial designs, 20 or which were at random, it was possible to obtain designs which compared favorably in terms of net benefits with the design actually adopted by the Corps of Engineers. These results attest to the efficiency of random and systematic sampling techniques when used in conjunction with computer simulation.

On the average, about $7\frac{1}{2}$ minutes of computer time were required to run a 250-year simulation, using synthetic traces of hydrology, for five demand periods. When the trace of actual hydrologic record was used, running time rose to 10 minutes for a simulation period of 90 years. This difference in running time attests to the efficiency of internal generation of hydrology (as done for the synthetic trace) over reading the hydrology from magnetic tape into the computer (which was necessary for the trace of actual record).

5 EXTENSION OF THE LEHIGH BASIN MODEL: THE DELAWARE BASIN SIMULATION MODEL

INTRODUCTION

The Delaware River simulation program is a step toward generalization of the Lehigh simulation program described in earlier chapters of this book. It expands the Lehigh routine to treat the much larger Delaware River system (shown in Fig. 5.1) of which the Lehigh is a subsystem; it handles new and complicated situations not present in the Lehigh design. The Delaware program is also an attempt to generalize the subroutines of the Lehigh program so as to render them readily applicable to river systems of various sizes and geometric configurations.

The Delaware program was coded simultaneously with the completion and testing of the Lehigh program, so that many of its techniques and procedures are similar to those of the Lehigh program; but there are notable differences. The Delaware program does not possess a complete flood algorithm; instead, it merely produces monthly flood peaks which may be analyzed by auxiliary programs or by manual computation. There is no operational hydrology generator in the Delaware program; hydrologic inflows are synthesized externally and are provided as input on magnetic tape. Finally, the operating policy differs considerably from that of the Lehigh program; details are given in this chapter.

OUTLINE OF THE SIMULATION PROCEDURE

Nineteen routines comprise the Delaware simulation program. The eighteen subprograms are coordinated by a main or Executive program. The Executive program, in common with its counterpart in the Lehigh simulation program, can initiate and supervise any number of consecutive independent simulation runs, a separate

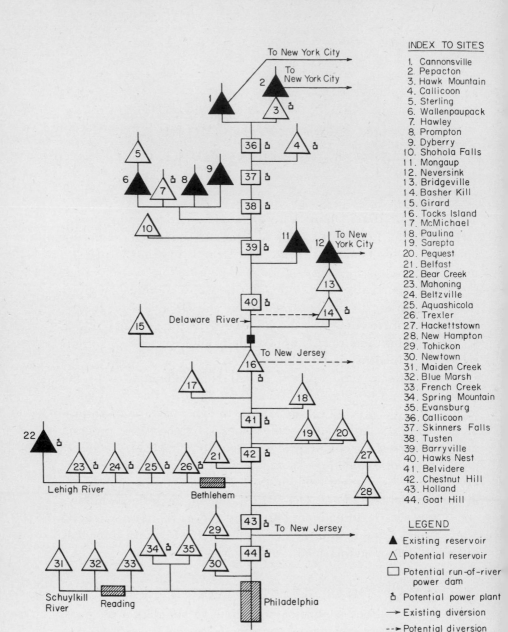

FIG. 5.1. Schematic diagram of Delaware River system.

simulation run being required for each unique combination of design variables. The sequence of steps in a single run is described in the following paragraphs and shown graphically in Fig. 5.2.

The Executive routine first calls Subroutine READ1 to read the permanent system data and the data which pertain to the first demand period of the run. Subroutine SETUPB is called to initialize the benefit evaluation procedure, and then the program performs the following algorithm, month by month, until the terminal month of the demand period is reached.

The hydrologic data for the current month are constructed in Subroutine READ1 by converting the input flows (at 25 gaging stations) to flows at 48 use points. After some preliminary computations, the Monthly Operating Algorithm—Subroutines BASIC, MONT, WATER, and POWER—is called. The Executive routine then summarizes the results of the Monthly Algorithm and calls Sub-

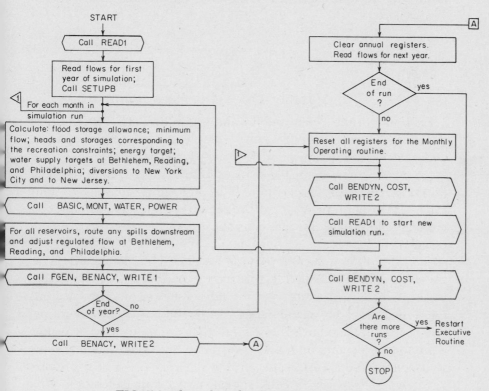

FIG. 5.2. Flow chart for Executive routine.

routine FGEN to generate flood peaks. The benefits for the month are evaluated by the Monthly Benefit Algorithm (Subroutine BENACM). If the current month terminates a year of the simulation, the Annual Benefit Algorithm (Subroutine BENACY) is called.

The Executive program cycles on a month-to-month basis until the end of the prescribed demand period is reached. Subroutines BENDYN and COST are then called to evaluate the benefits and costs for the entire demand period, after which Subroutine WRITE2 prints out a final summary. The next demand period now begins with the calling of Subroutine READ1. When the last demand period is completed, the Executive routine attempts to begin another simulation run; if none is scheduled, the program terminates.

While this procedure is similar to the general sequence of the Lehigh program, there are significant differences in the individual subroutines and the two basic algorithms — the Monthly Operating Algorithm and the Benefit Evaluation Algorithm — as described below.

THE SUBROUTINES IN DETAIL

The Monthly Operating Algorithm

Each month the Delaware simulation routine attempts to fulfill demands for water-supply and hydroelectric energy, subject to certain constraints on reservoir contents for flood-storage space and for recreation. The sequence of rules for this process comprises the Monthly Operating Algorithm. The Algorithm consists of four stages, each performed by a different subroutine. In addition, two general subroutines are called by these four for recurring types of tasks.

The Algorithm must first provide for inevitable flows — available water in excess of available reservoir capacity — and for basic releases, which incorporate the inevitable flows or provide for minimum discharges for maintenance of fish life and other amenities; this is accomplished in Subroutine BASIC. Subroutine MONT makes a number of exports from and transfers within the system. Diversions to the New York water-supply network occur at reservoirs 1, 2, and 12 (see Fig. 5.1). A special target flow (set by the U.S. Supreme Court) is specified for Montague, above reservoir 16

(Tocks Island). If the Supreme Court target is not met by natural flows, supplementary releases must be made from reservoirs 1, 2, and 12. If flow at Montague exceeds the Supreme Court target, a diversion to reservoir 14 (Basher Kill) may be possible. The maximum possible diversion to Basher Kill is always made because the diverted flow can be used to produce additional power at reservoir 14. Subroutine WATER makes two other diversions from the basin to New Jersey.

The third task of the Monthly Operating Algorithm is to meet water-supply targets at the three use points: Bethlehem (on the Lehigh), Reading (on the Schuylkill), and Philadelphia (on the lower Delaware below all storage sites). Subroutine WATER attempts to meet these requirements according to the following operating rule. Reservoirs 22 through 26, on the Lehigh, are first tapped to meet the target at Bethlehem while reservoirs 31 and 32 attempt to satisfy the target at Reading. The lower Delaware system, comprising reservoir 16 (Tocks Island) and all reservoirs below it (except those on the Lehigh and the Schuylkill), is then called upon to meet the requirement at Philadelphia. In this computation, reservoir 16 and all the reservoirs above it are combined and considered as a single reservoir. If the lower Delaware system cannot meet the target at Philadelphia, the Lehigh and Schuylkill systems are called upon for additional water. A deficit persisting after these withdrawals causes the program to abandon the first constraint levels, which limit the draft from each reservoir, and substitute a new and possibly lower set of constraints. The additional water now available is allocated according to the same procedure.

Energy generation is controlled by Subroutine POWER. Since the release through the turbine is not an explicit function of the energy output of a power plant, Subroutine POWER cannot make releases in a straightforward manner but must try to meet the energy target by a series of approximations to the correct releases. The centrally located reservoir 16 is first called to meet the energy requirement, and then followed by the other power-producing reservoirs. Iteration continues until the energy output is closer to the target than a specific tolerance, or until no more energy can be generated.

The two general subroutines, BOX and SPACE, perform the bookkeeping tasks associated with a release. Subroutine BOX computes the basic release and, when necessary, makes those supplementary releases specified by the calling routine. In addition, BOX computes the power generated by all releases. Subroutine SPACE applies the space-rule algorithm, described in Chapter 3, to withdraw a prescribed quantity of water from any set of reservoirs. Both subroutines are perfectly general and can be used for any system or configuration of reservoirs.

Subroutine BOX (Fig. 5.3)

(1) In the first pass through Subroutine BOX, basic releases are computed. The basic release is set equal to the contents in excess of the flood-storage level. If the basic release is not as large as the required minimum flow, the first supplementary release attempts to meet the requirement. This constitutes the basic release computation.

(2) The number of the reservoir being tapped is set by the calling program, exogenous to Subroutine BOX. The contents of this reservoir (reservoir J) are updated. Another exogenous variable informs Subroutine BOX whether the upper or lower constraint is in force, whereupon the amount of available water in reservoir J is computed as the excess over the constraint level. The program now attempts to release that amount of water prescribed by the exogenously generated requirement. Subroutine BOX does not designate this release as supplementary release one, two, or three, reserving this decision to the calling program.

(3) If reservoir J has a power plant, the following computations are performed. The fraction of the month during which the contents of reservoir J exceed dead-storage level is computed and the average head is taken as a polynomial function of the average contents. The effective power flow is the total amount of water flowing from reservoir J, limited by the associated turbine capacity. The energy generated, U, is computed by the formula

$$U = E \cdot H \cdot T \cdot F,$$

where E is the efficiency of the power plant, H the average head, T the time above dead storage, and F the effective power flow. The energy computations for a run-of-river power plant are simplified because it has a fixed head.

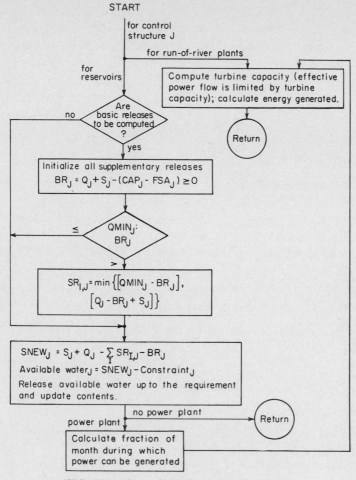

FIG. 5.3. Flow chart for subroutine BOX.

(4) After the energy is computed, control returns to the calling program.

Subroutine SPACE (Fig. 5.4)

(1) The space rule for allocating releases among multiple reservoirs is

$$\text{Allocation}_J = \text{Contents}_J - \text{Capacity}_J +$$
$$+ \frac{[\Sigma_J(\text{Capacity}_J - \text{Contents}_J) + \text{Release Requirement}] \cdot \text{Future Inflow}_J}{\Sigma_J \text{Future Inflow}_J}$$

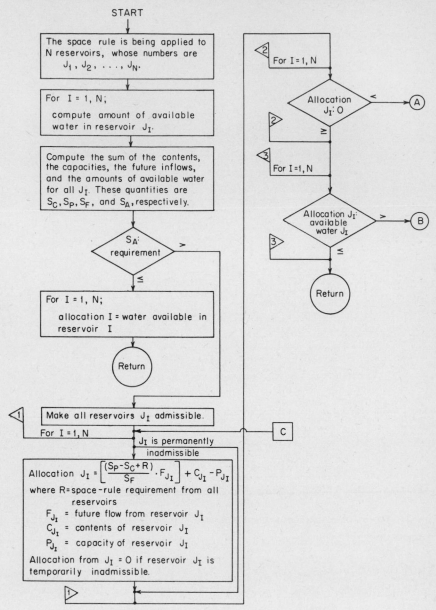

FIG. 5.4. Flow chart for subroutine SPACE.

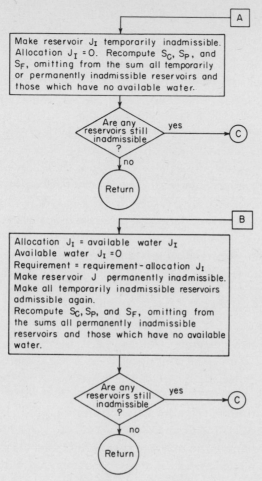

FIG. 5.4 (continued).

The program calling Subroutine SPACE establishes a list of reservoirs to which the space rule is to be applied, and sets the requirement—the amount of water to be drawn—from these reservoirs. This means that Subroutine SPACE is completely general; it can be applied to a large system to make allocations from many reservoirs, limited only by the computer's storage capacity.

(2) The constraint currently in force on the system determines the amount of water available for release in each reservoir. If the sum of these amounts falls short of the requirement, the space rule is not applied; the maximum amount of available water is re-

leased from each reservoir and control returns to the calling location.

(3) If excess water is available, the program proceeds into the main space-rule loop (steps 3–6). The basic allocation equation is applied to each reservoir selected by the calling program; the allocation, however, is made only over those reservoirs which are "admissible." The first time through the loop, all reservoirs are admissible, no matter what has occurred in previous space-rule allocations; as succeeding steps are reached, various reservoirs may be rendered temporarily or permanently inadmissible.

(4) The allocations made in step 3 are checked in two ways. A negative allocation to any reservoir sends control to step 5. If no negative allocations are made, the program examines each reservoir and determines whether its allocation exceeds its available water. A violation transfers control to step 6. If there are no unacceptable allocations, the result is satisfactory and control returns to the calling location.

(5) If reservoir J has a negative allocation in step 3 it is made temporarily inadmissible and the program returns to step 3. Thus all reservoirs with negative releases are eliminated, one by one, from the allocation. If at any point there are no admissible reservoirs, further allocation would be useless, so control returns to the calling location.

(6) When all negative allocations are eliminated by step 5, control passes to this step if any allocation is too large. In this event, all available water in the relevant reservoir is allocated, the requirement for the whole system is reduced by the amount of this irreversible allocation, and the reservoir is made inadmissible for the duration of this application of the space rule. All reservoirs which had formerly been made temporarily inadmissible because of negative allocations are now restored to the system, and the cycle begins again. If at any point no admissible reservoirs are left, the program terminates and control returns to the calling location.

Thus the program is limited in the number of loops it can execute. Assuming an allocation among n reservoirs, at worst $n-1$ of the initial allocations can be negative, so $n-1$ passes are required to eliminate them temporarily, and another pass is needed to eliminate the reservoir with the excessive positive allocation. Then $n-2$ allocations may be negative, and so on. Thus the program can recycle at most $\frac{1}{2}n(n + 1)$ times before making a satisfactory allocation; in practice, this rarely happens.

Subroutine BASIC

Subroutine BASIC instructs Subroutine BOX as to which reservoirs have power plants, and computes, as input to Subroutine BOX, the inflows to downstream reservoirs and power plants as a consequence of basic releases from upstream reservoirs made in Subroutine BOX.

(1) The first recreation constraint level is put into effect at all reservoirs.

(2) Subroutine BOX is called to make basic releases from the reservoirs farthest upstream (reservoirs 1 and 2).

(3) Upon return of control from Subroutine BOX, the inflow to reservoir 3 (which is downstream from reservoir 2) is incremented to account for the basic release made from reservoir 2.

(4) Subroutine BOX is called again, this time to make basic releases from reservoirs 3, 4, and 5.

(5) When control returns to Subroutine BASIC, the process of alternately correcting inflows to downstream reservoirs and calling Subroutine BOX, is continued until basic releases are made in all 25 reservoirs.

(6) The corrected inflow for the farthest upstream run-of-river power plant is computed and Subroutine BOX is called to make the energy computation for this plant.

(7) Upon return of control from Subroutine BOX, corrected inflow for the next downstream run-of-river power plant is computed and Subroutine BOX is called to compute the energy generation at this plant.

(8) This process is repeated until inflows and energy generation are computed for all run-of-river power plants, whence control returns to the calling location.

Subroutine MONT (Fig. 5.5)

(1) The regulated flow at Montague is computed. If it exceeds the Supreme Court target, control passes to step 2; if it is less, control passes to step 3; if it just equals the target, control passes to step 5.

(2) The diversion to Basher Kill (reservoir 14) is computed; it

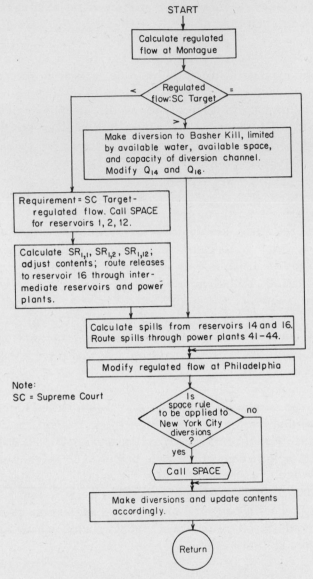

START

Calculate regulated flow at Montague

Regulated flow:SC Target

Make diversion to Basher Kill, limited by available water, available space, and capacity of diversion channel. Modify Q_{14} and Q_{16}.

Requirement = SC Target− regulated flow. Call SPACE for reservoirs 1, 2, 12.

Calculate $SR_{1,1}$, $SR_{1,2}$, $SR_{1,12}$; adjust contents; route releases to reservoir 16 through intermediate reservoirs and power plants.

Calculate spills from reservoirs 14 and 16. Route spills through power plants 41−44.

Modify regulated flow at Philadelphia

Note: SC = Supreme Court

Is space rule to be applied to New York City diversions ?

no

yes

Call SPACE

Make diversions and update contents accordingly.

Return

FIG. 5.5. Flow chart for subroutine MONT.

cannot exceed the flow at the point of diversion, the excess flow at Montague, the capacity of the diversion channel or the remaining capacity in reservoir 14. Control passes to step 4.

(3) A space-rule allocation is made among reservoirs 1, 2, and 12

to meet the Supreme Court deficit. Reservoir 2 is in series with reservoir 3; reservoir 12 is in series with reservoirs 13 and 14; and 1, 2, and 12 are all in series with reservoir 16. Thus the releases must be routed downstream and added to the flows at the run-of-river power plants on the main stem of the Delaware between reservoirs 2 and 16.

(4) The contents of reservoirs 14 and 16 are updated, and power is computed by Subroutine BOX. The releases are then routed through the lower Delaware to Philadelphia by way of power plants 41–44.

(5) The regulated flow at Philadelphia is computed for use by Subroutine WATER.

(6) Diversions to New York City are made. An input variable instructs the program whether to make individual releases from reservoirs 1, 2, and 12, or to apportion a single requirement among all three. When the New York City diversions are completed, control returns to the calling location.

Subroutine WATER

(1) After making the specified diversion from reservoir 16 to New Jersey and initializing the upper constraint level, Subroutine WATER attempts to meet the water-supply target at Bethlehem. Storage in reservoir 22 is tapped to meet the target, and if it is insufficient the remaining deficit is apportioned among reservoirs 23–26 by the space rule. The process is repeated at the second constraint level if unsuccessful at the first.

(2) To meet the water-supply target at Reading, allocations are made subject to the upper constraint. The space rule attempts to meet the target from reservoirs 31 and 32 and goes to the lower constraint if there is not enough water. The program next makes the diversion to New Jersey below power plant 43 through the Raritan canal and updates flows affected by the releases made in steps 1 and 2.

(3) If the current flow at Philadelphia is below its target value, the space rule attempts to make up the difference from the Lower Delaware reservoirs, excluding the Lehigh and the Schuylkill. This computation is performed as if the entire Upper Delaware and reservoir 16 were a single reservoir, with fictitious contents,

capacity, constraint levels, and so on, equal to the sums of the respective quantities for the individual reservoirs.

(4) If the Lower Delaware (space-rule) allocation meets the water-supply target, the corresponding releases are made. The program then restores the state of the Upper Delaware system, which was consolidated into one reservoir in step 3, and applies the space rule to distribute the Upper Delaware release among the individual reservoirs. In this computation, reservoirs in series (1 and 2; 5 and 6; 12, 13, and 14) are again consolidated. Control then returns to the calling location.

(5) If the Lower Delaware space-rule allocation does not yield enough water, the Lehigh and Schuylkill systems are again drawn upon by the space rule. If the target can now be met, flows at Bethlehem and Reading are updated and control returns to the calling program via step 4. If there is still not enough water, control goes to step 6.

(6) The program repeats the Lower Delaware space-rule allocation under the second constraint. If enough water is now available, flows at Bethlehem and Reading must be updated before control returns to the calling location via step 4. A persisting deficit transfers control to step 7.

(7) At this point available water can be drawn only from the Lehigh-Schuylkill system at its lower constraint. A space-rule allocation is made, the deficit or excess is recorded, flows are updated, and control returns via step 4.

Subroutine POWER

(1) The total energy attributed to releases for other purposes is calculated. If this satisfies the requirement, or if there is no water left to produce additional energy, no further releases are made and control returns to the calling location.

(2) If the system had been forced to use the lower recreation constraint earlier in the current month, control goes to step 10 to adjust constraint levels.

(3) Otherwise, the constraint level at each power-producing reservoir is increased, if necessary, so that flows in excess of turbine capacities are not released, thereby saving water which would otherwise bypass the turbines.

(4) A trial release from reservoir 16 to meet the energy target is computed. The power generated at run-of-river power plants and the variation of the head at each reservoir must be considered in this computation.

(5) Subroutine BOX makes the reservoir 16 trial release described in step 4 and determines the total energy generated. Because the correct release cannot be computed explicitly, the trial release may not meet the energy requirement within the specified tolerance. If it does, control returns via step 12; if not, the program proceeds to step 6.

(6) If excess energy is produced, a negative adjustment is computed; control returns to step 5 to reduce the previous release and again make the power test. If a deficit occurs, the program determines if earlier in the process reservoir 16 alone had yielded an energy excess. If so, repetition of the iterative process via step 4 will converge to the target. If not, the program attempts to meet the target by releasing all water available from reservoir 16. If this fails twice, reservoir 16 cannot meet the energy target by itself, so control passes to step 7 for the next attempt.

(7) A trial release from all the power-producing reservoirs (except reservoir 16) is computed as before, and Subroutine SPACE is called to distribute this release among the reservoirs. Power is computed and the tolerance test is made again. If the target is reached, control returns to the calling location via step 12; if not, an excess transfers control to step 8, a deficit to step 9.

(8) The estimate of releases for power being too large, the process is repeated with a smaller estimate, and the effects of the previous allocations are annulled. Control returns to step 7.

(9) The space-rule allocation can be repeated with a revised estimate if more than one reservoir has water available. If so, control returns to step 7. If no reservoir has water available, control goes to step 10; if a single reservoir has water available, to step 11.

(10) No reservoirs have water available, so no more energy can be generated at the current constraint level. If the system is at the upper constraint level, the lower set of constraints is substituted and the process is repeated starting with step 3. If the lower constraint level has already been reached, the routine terminates and control returns via step 12.

(11) Reservoir J, the only reservoir with water available, can be

used to meet the energy target exactly as for reservoir 16, in steps 4–6. A successful allocation transfers control to step 12, but failure to meet the target results in an examination of the constraint level, step 10.

(12) The excess or deficit in energy is recorded and control returns to the calling location.

The Benefit Algorithm

Subroutine SETUPB

(1) The total annual water-supply targets at Bethlehem, Reading, and Philadelphia, and the total annual energy target are computed. The net annual water-supply targets for the three cities are the differences between these targets and the minimum historic flow rate. The nominal benefits for water supply and for energy are then computed as polynomial functions of these targets.

(2) The nominal recreation attendance, in visitor-days for each reservoir, is a function of the total reservoir capacity less the average flood storage allowance for the months of July and August. The nominal benefits for recreation at each reservoir are computed as a polynomial function of the nominal recreation attendance; the nominal recreation benefit for the system is the sum of these benefits over all reservoirs.

(3) The accumulating registers for various quantities are initialized to zero.

(4) Control returns to the calling location.

Subroutine BENACM

(1) If there is an energy deficit in the current month, its value is accumulated and the counter which registers the total number of deficits is incremented. If the deficit exceeds a specified percentage of the energy target, another register is incremented. The monthly energy loss, a polynomial function of the deficit, is computed and added to the sum of monthly energy losses.

(2) If there is excess energy, the dump-energy benefits, a polynomial function of the excess energy, are computed and accumulated. If the energy excess exceeds a specified percentage of the target, another counter is incremented.

(3) For each of the three water-supply systems — Lehigh, Schuylkill, and Delaware —

(a) the water-supply deficit or excess is accumulated;
(b) if there is a water-supply deficit, the water-supply losses are computed as a function of the percentage of deficit; and
(c) the square of the water-supply loss is accumulated for subsequent calculation of the standard deviation.

(4) For each reservoir, recreation losses are computed as follows. If the initial and terminal contents of the reservoir are at or above the total capacity less the flood-storage-allowance (the long-term storage level), the recreation loss is zero. If not, the initial and terminal heads are computed. If the reservoir is below this level at the start and end of the month, the recreation loss is a function of the average drawdown from this level. If, on the other hand, the water level is above the long-term storage level for part of the month and below it for the rest, the recreation loss must be multiplied by the fraction of the month during which the reservoir contents are below the long-term storage level.

(5) The recreation loss at each reservoir is accumulated in the annual recreation loss register.

(6) For each reservoir, the final monthly contents are expressed as a percentage of capacity, and a counter corresponding to that decile of capacity is incremented. The registers recording the maximum and minimum contents attained by each reservoir are updated, and each reservoir's counters for spills and depletions are incremented if necessary.

(7) The following registers are updated or incremented as appropriate: number of times the Supreme Court target is missed; number of floods; maximum peak at Bethlehem, Riegelsville, Belvidere, Port Jervis, Trenton, and Schuylkill at Philadelphia; maximum energy deficit; maximum water-supply deficit at Bethlehem, Reading, and Philadelphia; maximum yearly recreation loss; and maximum energy excess. The sum of energy excess is accumulated.

(8) Control returns to the calling location.

Subroutine BENACY

(1) The following counters are incremented, as necessary: number of annual deficits at Bethlehem, Reading, and Philadelphia;

number of annual recreation deficits; number of annual energy excesses.

(2) The annual benefits for water supply at the three locations and for recreation are given by the differences between the several nominal benefits and the associated total annual losses. The annual energy benefits are the nominal benefits for energy plus the difference between dump-energy benefits and energy losses.

(3) The following quantities and their squares are accumulated where indicated: total excess energy for the year; total energy deficits for the year; total of water-supply benefits at Bethlehem, Reading, and Philadelphia; annual benefits for energy and recreation; annual water-supply benefits at Bethlehem, Reading, and Philadelphia.

(4) For a discounted run, the following quantities, discounted at ten interest rates (0, 2, $2\frac{1}{2}$, 3, $3\frac{1}{2}$, 4, $4\frac{1}{2}$, 5, $5\frac{1}{2}$, and 6 percent) are accumulated: annual energy benefits; annual water-supply benefits at Bethlehem, Reading, and Philadelphia; annual recreation benefits; and gross benefits (sum of the preceding five quantities).

(5) The value and the square of the value of the gross annual benefits are accumulated.

(6) Control returns to the calling location.

Subroutine BENDYN

(1) Factors for discounting benefits to present value are calculated.

(2) For an undiscounted run, benefits accumulated in Subroutine BENACY are adjusted to present value.

(3) Control returns to the calling location.

Subroutine COST

(1) The capital cost of each reservoir is computed as a function of of its capacity, and the OMR cost as a function of the capital cost.

(2) For each reservoir with a variable-head power plant, the capital cost of the power plant is $P^{0.866}f_1(R) + f_2(P)$, where f_1 and f_2 are polynomial functions, P is the power capacity, and R is the rated head. The OMR cost is a function of the power plant capacity.

(3) For each reservoir, the recreation capital cost is $g[(A)(C)]$,

where g is a polynomial function, A is the average recreation attendance during the summer months, and C is the average long-term storage pool in the reservoir in the summer. The recreation OMR cost of each reservoir is proportional to the capital cost for recreation.

(4) Total costs are computed; control returns to calling location.

The Input-Output Algorithm

Subroutine READ1

(1) The first section of Subroutine READ1 reads the permanent parameters of the system from the system input tape. The values may be copied onto the Monitor System output tape if desired.

(2) Reservoir capacities and other quantities which vary in different demand periods are read in the next segment of the routine.

(3) The final part of Subroutine READ1 converts input flows at 25 gaging stations, which are read from a special input tape by the Executive routine, to flows at 35 reservoirs, nine run-of-river power plants, and four water-supply target points.

(4) Control returns to the calling location.

Subroutine WRITE1

An input variable instructs this subroutine to select among printing monthly summaries, printing summaries only in flood months, and not printing at all. If a flood occurs, values of the flood peaks are always punched and saved for possible manual analysis or inclusion in another program.

Subroutine WRITE2

(1) If instructed by an input card, this subroutine prepares a condensed report of the economic benefits and losses of the past twelve months, and a display of the discounted benefit values accumulated thus far.

(2) At the conclusion of the simulation run a final summary is printed. Gross and net benefits for the entire run are computed and printed for each of ten discount rates.

The Flood Algorithm

A complete flood algorithm for the Delaware system is not available. In addition to the time required to develop a new flood model, inclusion of such a set of programs might exceed the 7094 memory capacity, 80 percent of which is utilized by the present program. Subroutine FGEN of the current program, however, is available for estimating flood peaks. Peaks are computed at each of the 35 reservoirs; at the nine power plants; at Montague, Bethlehem, Reading, and Philadelphia; and at four other locations. The peaks are calculated according to the formula

$$p_j = \exp_{10}(a_j + b_j(\log_{10} q_j) + c_j r_j),$$

where p_j is the peak at location j; q_j is the monthly flow at location j; r_j is a normal random sampling deviate; and a_j, b_j, and c_j are parameters which vary cyclically from month to month for each site.

CONCLUDING COMMENTS

Much new information has been gained from this adaptation of the Lehigh simulation program to the larger Delaware system, particularly from the experience in devising new subroutines and algorithms. For example, Subroutine BOX turns out to be extremely effective in reducing coding difficulty and computer time when used for releases to meet water-supply and energy targets and to compute energy generated from releases; however, it is less effective in handling reservoir diversions and corresponding adjustments in inflows. The subroutine could be made more versatile by adding a "flow-through" option which would route inflows through the reservoir unchanged and compute the corresponding energy generation. One segment of Subroutine BOX used for computing basic releases (reservoir spills and releases necessary to meet minimum flow requirements) is logically independent of the main portion of the subroutine, and could well be set up as a separate subroutine.

Flexibility in coding and system operation could also be improved by removing the limit on the number of recreation constraint levels which the programs can accommodate.

Data preparation. The greatest data difficulty we encountered arose from derivation of polynomial coefficients for the various functional relationships in the system (for example, head-capacity curves). Luckily, most of our functions were manageable, and were fitted by a modified version of PYFT, a program available from the SHARE organization. Relationships involving segmented curves (for example, a loss function where a constant loss is assumed for values of the argument greater than a certain limit) cannot be well fitted throughout their entire domain, and have to be specifically programmed into the system.

Computer speed. The Delaware River system has approximately six times the number of design variables as the Lehigh, but it has been possible to keep the running time of the Delaware program on the computer to only three to four times that of the Lehigh program. This has been accomplished through greater generalization and streamlining of coding, use of specialized subroutines such as BOX, GM, and SPACE; and conversion of some of the most frequently used subroutines into FAP language. An average computer time per year of simulation of 7 or 8 seconds has been attained—that is, 6.25 minutes for 50 years of simulation. These times are exclusive of initial and final input-output manipulation, which consumes approximately 0.3 minutes per run. For any one simulation run, unusual simulation conditions may result in times significantly above the average (for example, if the energy computations in Subroutine POWER take a very long time to converge).

Generality. In adapting the Lehigh program to the Delaware program, significant progress has been made in the generalization of various simulation techniques. The generalized subroutines developed for the Delaware program can be adapted to a wide variety of river systems without extensive reprogramming. Generalization lies primarily in programming concepts rather than in the details of array sizes and other specifics. Following is a classification of the major subroutines of the Delaware simulation program by degree of generality.

1. *Highly generalized:*
    Subroutines BENACM, BENACY, BENDYN, BOX, GM, SETUPB, and SPACE.
2. *Moderately generalized:*
    Subroutine COST, generalized except for computations involving power plants.

Subroutine POWER contains generalized algorithm for meeting power requirements from one or more reservoirs; subroutine as a whole is specific.

Subroutine WATER contains generalized algorithm for meeting water-supply requirement from one or more reservoirs, but subroutine as a whole is specific.

3. *Specific:*

Subroutines BASIC, FGEN, MONT, and the Executive routine.

6 LESSONS AND PROSPECTS

The effectiveness of simulation depends not so much upon a good man *and* a good computer as upon the successful and flexible interplay between man and machine. This is necessarily influenced by the sophistication of the current generation of computers and the current modes of communication between the analyst and his machine. The state of the art is changing rapidly; as this is written (1965) newly announced machines may initiate far-reaching changes in computing. Just as our early attempts to simulate the behavior of river systems on UNIVAC I now appear totally inadequate, future designers may wonder how we persevered with the IBM 7094 computer and the FORTRAN II compiler.

MAN

In computing jargon there is a distinction between *analyst* and *programmer*. The analyst devises algorithms, specifies the nature of the numerical techniques to be employed, and evaluates the reliability of the output. The results of his labors are (i) a flow chart of the program; (ii) the supplementary documents which justify the chosen algorithms; and (iii) a tabulation of the required data and their formats. Given these documents the programmer prepares the code in the relevant machine—or pseudo-language (for example, FORTRAN or ALGOL) which, when executed, solves the original problem. The flow chart and the associated algebraic formalisms are the principal means of communication between analyst and programmer. If these are perfectly executed, the analyst need not have any training in coding, while the programmer can be ignorant of the problem and its interpretation.[1] For example, in the numerical

[1] In practice the dichotomy is rarely achieved. Usually the analyst's knowledge of coding and of machine limitations influences the selection of algorithms and thereby—at least operationally—strongly influences the distinction between those problems which are "computable" and those which are not.

solution of a differential equation or the integration of an analytical function by numerical quadrature, it matters little if the programmer knows the underlying mathematical and physical structure because the required coding can be concisely summarized for him.

Simulation analysis demands a vastly different spectrum of communication. The detailed logical structure of the prototype system, and all of the relevant interconnections among its components, can rarely be stipulated before initiating and coding; thus, many adjustments and, indeed, fresh starts are required as the several segments of the model are debugged, tested, and finally validated. It is precisely during this critical period of program testing and evaluating that the traditional channels of communication between analyst and programmer are likely to break down. The jargons unique to each discipline—the language of the analyst's specialty and the mysterious mnemonic staccato of the programmer—are too widely divergent for smooth collaboration.

A solution to this dilemma is to eliminate the problem of communication by combining the functions of analyst and programmer into a single person.[2] To be sure, the supply of such persons is limited; the requisite disciplines, including civil engineering, hydrology, economics, statistics, programming, and numerical analysis, are sufficiently great in number and depth to effectively restrict those who possess the necessary background to a few university campuses and large research organizations. However, once the need for analysts with these unique qualifications becomes sufficiently acute, the necessary training can be provided by universities, by research organizations, and to some extent, by on-the-job experience. Simulation analysis of any large-scale water-resource system should be led by such an engineer-economist-programmer, with assistance from specialists in hydrology, civil engineering, economics, statistics, and computer programming.

MACHINE

It need hardly be said that a large and fast digital computer is essential for simulating all but the simplest of water-resource sys-

[2] We seemingly disregarded our own advice because the extension of the Lehigh River study to the Delaware was carried out by a programmer unversed in water-resource lore. But (i) he had the Lehigh model as the basis for his work, and (ii) our recommendation is based, in part, on experience with the Delaware program.

tems. The IBM 7094 has 32,768 directly addressable memory locations, whereas the capacity of the new generation of machines is
measured in millions of directly addressable locations. The Lehigh
program uses all but a few memory locations of the IBM 7094, so
that particular care was required during testing and validating the
program lest the simplest program change exceed the capacity of
core storage. Many simulation features, omitted from the Lehigh
program, could be readily accommodated on newer machines because of their greater internal speed and storage capacity. Subroutines for low-flow operation, for water-quality management, and
for automatic (e.g., random or systematic) specification of design
variables are not incorporated in the final program because of
storage limitations.

But an excellent computer is only as useful as its ready accessibility. If the computing installation is administered under a system
of rigid priorities unfavorable to the simulation analyst, or if the
machine and its peripheral equipment are simply unable to remain abreast of the workload, turn-around time[3] may be intolerably
long. In these circumstances, particularly for simulation programs
which require frequent trial runs to test their many branches, debugging and testing times would become excessive. At our Computing Center one can expect to make three runs a day, so that
troublesome routines can be debugged in short order. Delays of a
week, however, are not uncommon at some installations; such a
queue would virtually preclude the use of simulation on the scale
exemplified in our Lehigh program.

Although the typical university computing installation, characterized by its research orientation and rapid turn-around time,
is ideally suited for development and testing of simulation programs, university research efforts are frequently overcome by the
enormous task of collecting, tabulating, and key-punching the
requisite data. However, a planning agency, with adequate resources and supporting staff, could quickly surmount the problem
of data manipulation and punching; for this task the agency is far
better equipped than its counterpart at a university.

With respect to scheduling, completion dates must be imposed

---

[3] Turn-around time is the elapsed time from the moment the program deck is
deposited or batched at the computer installation to the moment the finished output
is returned.

realistically and administered flexibly. Apart from initial data-processing, simulation analysis involves frequent recoding and recompilation of subroutines that appear to be operating correctly. These changes arise from difficulties in devising *a priori* a model which consistently and adequately represents reality, so that determination of the adequacy of a subroutine might require execution of the entire program. Given this need for trial and retrial, it is imprudent to establish a rigid time schedule under which the constituent phases of the program must be completed.

FLEXIBILITY OF THE PROGRAM

When the flow-charting and coding of the Lehigh system was initiated, it was our hope that the program would be highly general and highly flexible. Except for the unifying thread of a MAIN Program coded to account for the particular spatial and temporal relationships among reservoirs, each subroutine or group of subroutines would perform its task of releasing water, generating inputs, computing hydroelectric power, and the like, without reference to the particular geometric configuration of reservoirs in the Lehigh system. But in fact the complexity of the Lehigh system, especially the alternative power diversions reflected by our five alternative Cases, defeated our attempt to achieve this high degree of generality.

As the coding of the Lehigh simulation progressed, and as segments became more and more intricate, our objective of maintaining generality became less attainable as we were forced to treat matters of reservoir configuration (Case number) in the general routines rather than in the MAIN Program. Thus the subroutines became less general and more nearly oriented to the particular problems of the Lehigh system. We compromised with the goal of generality in order to produce a working program more readily. To achieve generality, the problem would be recast to incorporate into the MAIN Program all decisions pertaining to reservoir configuration. For the Lehigh system this would mean five MAIN Programs, one for each Case, one or another of which would accompany each run.

PROSPECTS FOR APPLICATION

To what extent should simulation be used as an analytical technique in water-resource planning, and at what stages in the planning process should the technique be applied? To help answer these questions, we digress briefly to sketch the main steps of the process of water-resource planning, development, and operation.[4]

1. Reconnaissance, or framework analyses, including
   (a) broad studies and projections of demands and resources;
   (b) inventory of major development and management alternatives; and
   (c) preliminary screening of development and management alternatives to select the most promising measures for analysis under detailed system planning.
2. Detailed system planning leading to adoption of development and management programs, including
   (a) further screening of development and management elements identified in Step 1; and
   (b) systems analysis of selected development and management elements, leading to selection of an optimal plan.
3. Detailed project design based on adoption of system plan.
4. Operation of the completed system.

Reconnaissance stage. Early in the reconnaissance stage, simulation has no important application in compiling the inventory of alternative development and management possibilities. There is little systems analysis applied in the mere cataloging of reservoir sites, power development possibilities, and measures for controlling land and water use, which is the essence of this early step.

The preliminary screening segment of the reconnaissance stage offers some opportunity for simulation. Unfortunately, there are often so many alternative development possibilities at this stage, even after obviously inferior alternatives are deleted, that detailed simulation (such as that described in this book) is infeasible. Our work on Delaware basin simulation indicates that, with present

[4] For a detailed discussion of the water-resource planning process, see M. Hufschmidt, "Field-level planning of water-resource systems," *Journal of Water Resources Research, 1,* 147 (1965).

computer capacities, as many as 50 development alternatives can be handled in a detailed simulation analysis. A considerably larger number of alternatives could be accommodated if the simulation program were stripped of some of its features, with consequent sacrifice of realism. These limits can be extended with the new generation of computers, but because the complexities and difficulties of coding increase rapidly with system size, detailed simulation appears unsuited for use in preliminary screening. The grossly simplified simulation technique outlined in the following paragraphs suggests an area for further research.

The essence of the simplified simulation technique consists of constructing storage-yield contours for each potential site. Unlike the related traditional storage-yield functions based on Rippl analysis (routing) of historical flows, the contours represent various levels of fulfillment and are based on the statistical properties of the storage-yield relation. Figure 6.1 shows a sector of the storage-yield surface for a typical reservoir.

In the proposed technique a storage-yield contour is developed at each site and the effects of cascading sites (that is, of sites in series and parallel) are determined by statistical procedures (convolution, for example) currently under investigation. Then, by comparing cascades with output obtained from individual sites, those units which add little output or little incremental reliability can be eliminated from the plan. Significant progress has been made on this technique, and its prospects in the planning process are favorable.

Detailed planning stage. At this stage, leading to adoption of a development plan, simulation is likely to find its greatest use. By this time the number of alternatives in a typical system is apt to be manageably small—50 or fewer. The results of supporting studies of topography, geology, land use, costs of facilities, and economics of demand are likely to be available in adequate detail to serve as inputs to the simulation, in the form of coefficients of system design variables, parameters and constants. The simulation analysis of the Lehigh system is suitable for application at this point in the planning process. Based on our favorable experience with the technique, we recommend its use in actual planning situations.

Detailed project design. At this stage of detailed engineering design immediately prior to construction, simulation can best be used

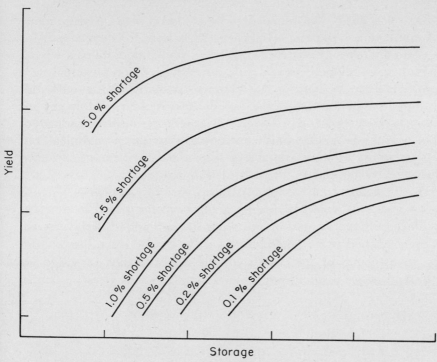

Yield

5.0 % shortage

2.5 % shortage

1.0 % shortage

0.5 % shortage

0.2 % shortage

0.1 % shortage

Storage

FIG. 6.1. Storage-yield contours at several levels of reliability.

to test the performance of alternative project and system designs. In fact, a simulation program written for the planning phase could probably be reused with minor modifications. If no such program exists, it may be profitable to develop one; such a program would be especially useful where more than one water-storage or control facility is contemplated and where system operating policy is crucial to the design of components. For large projects, with capital costs exceeding $50 million, for example, it would seem that substantial investment of time and money in design studies, including simulation analysis, can be readily justified.

Operation of completed systems. Simulation appears ideally suited to test a wide range of operating policies for existing systems. Such simulations would be of a different character from design studies. They would be more detailed and realistic with regard to the internal operation of the system, largely because many of the system parameters, including sizes of structures, would be fixed rather than variable.

One possibility that remains to be explored is the development of simulation programs to serve as tools both for design and for system operation. Few river systems in the United States are completely undeveloped; none is fully developed. The typical planning problem is to fit additional elements optimally into a partly developed system, and a master simulation program capable of handling both existing and prospective elements seems to be indicated. Because the program would continue to provide an analytical tool for operating existing systems, a substantial investment could be justified. Once coded, the simulation model would serve as a superior design tool for analysis of proposed investments because each new unit would be tested under conditions nearly identical with those which would obtain were the unit added to the system. The combined use of simulation for design and operation should be investigated in the context of the opportunities provided by rapid advances in computer technology.

APPENDICES   INDEX

APPENDIX I. LEGEND FOR FLOW CHARTS

 Start of Loop i; index is J, limits of index are h and k.

 Terminus of Loop i.

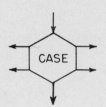 Multi-point conditional transfer, as for Case number.

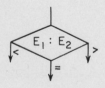 Conditional transfer based on comparison of magnitudes of expression E_1 and E_2.

 Computation or input-output.

 Unconditional transfer to entry point A.

Entry point A.

 Unconditional transfer and return to another sub-routine, as for SUPPOW.

 Unconditional return to the calling routine.

APPENDIX II. GLOSSARY OF FORTRAN SYMBOLS USED IN FLOW CHARTS

ADDSR — additional supplementary release from reservoir 1 or 2 routed through turbine 3 (reservoir 3) — constrained by channel or turbine capacity (10^2 acre ft).

AVHD — average head of reservoirs 3–6, used for preliminary computation of the required release (ft).

AVTIME — average fraction of a month during which reservoirs 3-6 are at or above the dead storage levels — used to estimate the release required to meet the target output for energy.

BASIC — subroutine of the Monthly Algorithm.

BR — basic release, or inevitable flow necessary to keep contents at flood storage level, for reservoirs 1–6 (10^2 acre ft).

CAP — reservoir capacity, reservoirs 1–6 (10^2 acre ft).

DEAD — dead storage, associated with turbines 1–9 (10^2 acre ft).

DENOM — sum of future flows (FUFLO) for reservoirs for which space-rule allocations are to be made (10^2 acre ft).

DIVERT — subroutine of the Monthly Algorithm.

DUMP — energy produced in excess of target output for energy (mwh).

EFFPOW — effective power flow, turbines 1–9 (10^2 acre ft).

ENERGY — energy generated at each of the 9 turbines (mwh).

EXCESS — non-negative difference between the inevitable flow and the minimum flow requirement (10^2 acre ft).

FSA — space allocated to flood-control storage, reservoirs 1–6 (10^2 acre ft).

FUFLO — future flows (over remainder of the drawdown-refill period), reservoirs 3–6, corresponding to each month, for use in the space rule (10^2 acre ft).

HARB — fixed heads associated with penstocks 7, 8, or 9 (ft).

HAVG — average head at the turbines 1–9, computed from the average contents (ft).

HMAX — maximum head, power plants 1–9 (ft).

LLJ — index for making releases when all space allocations are constrained.

PNSTOK — penstock capacity for reservoirs 1 or 2 (10^2 acre ft).

POWER — subroutine of the Monthly Algorithm.

PREC — contents, reservoirs 1–6, above current constraint level, to meet target output for energy (10^2 acre ft).

Q — inflow to reservoirs 1–6 (10^2 acre ft).

QDIV — quantity of water available for diversion from the Lehigh to reservoir 3, subsequently limited by capacity of the diversion channel and available space in reservoir 3 (10^2 acre ft).

QMIN — minimum flow required below reservoirs 1–6 (10^2 acre ft).

QPEN — release available for transmission through the penstock (10^2 acre ft).

QQPEN — release actually made through the penstock, limited by the penstock capacity (10^2 acre ft).

QREC — amount of water available in reservoirs 1–6 above current constraint levels to meet water-supply target at Bethlehem (10^2 acre ft).

QT — flow at Tannery (10^2 acre ft).

REC — amount of water available above constraint levels in reservoirs 3–6, for allocation of releases in the space rule (10^2 acre ft).

RECST2 — contents, corresponding to the second recreation constraint level, reservoirs 1–6 (10^2 acre ft).

RECSTO — contents, corresponding to the first recreation constraint level, reservoirs 1–6 (10^2 acre ft).

S — initial contents, reservoirs 1–6 (10^2 acre ft).

SHORT — release needed to maintain required minimum flows after inevitable releases are made, reservoirs 1–6 (10^2 acre ft).

SLOP — volume of releases, reservoir 1 or 2, in excess of penstock capacity (10^2 acre ft).

$SNEW_J$ — current values of contents, reservoirs 1–6, during operation of the Monthly Algorithm (10^2 acre ft). At end of Monthly Algorithm, it is final reservoir contents.

SPACE — subroutine of the Monthly Algorithm.

SR — supplementary releases 1–3 from reservoirs 1–6 (10^2 acre ft).

SR_1 — release to meet minimum channel flows

SR_2 — release to meet target output for water supply at Bethlehem

SR_3 — release to meet target output for energy

SUMCAP — sum of total reservoir capacities of those reservoirs from which allocations remain to be made by the space rule (10^2 acre ft).

SUMNEW — sum of current contents of those reservoirs from which allocations remain to be made by the space rule (10^2 acre ft).

SUMREC — sum of the amounts of water available above constraint levels in reservoirs 3–6, for allocation by the space rule (10^2 acre ft).

SUPPOW — subroutine in the Monthly Algorithm.

T1 — fraction of the month during which reservoir contents are at or above dead storage.

TURBQ — water capacity of turbines 1–9 (10^2 acre ft).

WATER — subroutine in the Monthly Algorithm.

INDEX

Ackoff, R. L., 1n
Algol, 193
Algorithm, 17, 90, 193; annual benefit, 92, 133, 135, 174; benefit, 186; benefit evaluation, 174; flood, 92, 94, 125, 127, 152, 171, 190; hydrology, 91, 94, 95; input-output, 189; monthly, 91–96, 98, 132, 152; monthly benefit, 92, 94, 133, 174; monthly operating, 173, 174; output, 92, 136, 138; run benefit, 92, 133, 136
Alkalinity, 75
Allentown, Pa., 9
Allentown–Bethlehem zone, 72, 73
Allocation, 123, 124, 130, 131, 132, 180; dead storage, 159; space-rule, 184
Allowance, flood-storage, 125
Alternative, external, 56, 76
Alternative cost: as a measure of benefit, 56, 59–61, 166–67; function, 60
Analog, electric, 2
Analyses: benefit, 133; cost, 133; multivariate, 76; numerical, 194
Analyst, 193, 194
Aquashicola Creek, 25–28, 72
Aquashicola reservoir, 12, 13n, 96
Augmentation, flow, 76

Balderston, F. E., 158n
Basher Kill, 175, 181
Bear Creek reservoir, 11, 13n, 96, 159, 169
Beltzville pipe, 133
Beltzville reservoir, 12, 13n, 96
Belvidere, N.J., 187
Benefits: 3, 139, 174; annual, 133, 188; cost ratio, 169; discounted, 84–86; dump, 135; energy, 163–169; expected net, 156; flood-control, 70–73, 163–169; gross, 135, 188, 189; net, 3, 139, 189; nominal, 95, 186; nominal annual, 135; present value, 83–87; recreation, 163–169; water supply, 163–169

Benefit function: 54–77; hydroelectric power; irrigation, 68–69; long-run, 55, 57, 69; municipal and industrial water supply, 57; recreation, 65–67; two-element, 55; water quality, 75–77
Bethlehem, 9, 14, 20, 23–28, 73, 96, 126–132, 175, 183, 184, 187, 190; regulated flow, 106–107, 110; unregulated flow, 106
Bias, 156
Binary Coded Decimal (BCD), 25
Blend, 157
Blunders, 152
Boor, Carl de, 139n
Borbeau, J., 3n
Bugs, 152
Burden, R., 13n

Capacity, 123; channel, 24, 128, 130, 131; dead-storage, 33; design, 50; factor, 32; flood-storage, 24; hydroelectric power, 62–65; installed, 32, 137; long-term storage, 98; power, 159, 188; recreation, 66, 67; steam-electric, 62; thermal power, 62–65; turbine, 176; value, 62
Capital: cost-capacity functions, 43; cost curves, 89; costs, 43, 48, 83–87, 137, 138, 161–169, 188, 189
Card-punching, 25
Cascading, 198
Cases, 12
Charges, power-operating, 52
Climatology, 7
Coefficient: correlation, 16, 127; serial, 155, 156
Columbia River, 3n
Components, 18; interim replacement, 53; orthogonal, 18, 127; principal, 94, 96, 155; random additive, 17, 126; stochastic, 7
Computer: digital, 194, 195; electronic, 1, 2; IBM 7094, 195; speed of, 191
Consistency, 154

Constants, 29, 36
Constraint: minimum flow, 76; water-supply, 61; recreation-level, 159, 160
Consumer surplus, 60
Contents: average, 101; normal pool, 100
Continuity, 14, 153
Contours, storage-yield, 198
Control, 90
Convolution, 154
Corps of Engineers. See United States Army Corps of Engineers
Correlation: cross, 17; serial, 17, 155, 156; coefficients, 16, 94, 127
Correlograms, 155
Costs: 3, 43, 139, 174; capital, 43, 48, 83–87, 137, 138, 161–169, 188, 189; discontinuities, 45; external alternatives, 60, 61, 66; functions, 43; interim replacement, 53; maintenance, 43; OMR, 53, 83–87, 137, 138, 188; operation, 43; point estimates, of, 45; replacement, 43; specific power, 45; specific power facilities, 45; specific recreation facilities, 48; storage facilities, 43
Covariance, 154; matrix, 155, 156
Curve, recession, 21
Cycle, drawdown-refill, 123

Damage: 130, 131; discharge function, 71; flood, 9; annual flood, 135; stage function, 70
Dams, 9
Data: hydrologic, 24; hydrologic conversions, 24; missing flow, 19
Dead-storage allocation, 159
Decision-making, 23
Decision variables, 159
Deficits: 42, 186; energy, 168, 187; recreation, 168, 188; Supreme Court, 183; water-supply, 123, 168, 187
Delaware basin: report, 5n, 51n, 57, 73, 80n; simulation model, 171–192
Delaware River: 3, 19, 52, 53; basin, 171
Demand: 170; aggregate function, 57, 58; biochemical oxygen, 75; inelastic function, 59; period, 85–87, 158, 159; point estimate of, 57, 58; power, 7; ranges of, 58; water, 7, 59
Densities, spectral, 155
Design: least-cost, 60; optimal system, 158; power system, 46; project, 197
Design variables, 1, 29, 159, 173, 191; major, 30; subsidiary, 35; system, 4, 90
Deviate: standardized random, 16; standard normal, 127

Deviation, standard, 156, 157
Discount operator, 84, 87, 386
Discount rate, 136, 139, 189
Discounted benefits, 84–86
Discounted run, 136, 138, 168, 188
Discounting, 4, 83, 90, 135
Discrepancies, 152
Distribution: bivariate normal, 126; gamma, 16, 156; log-normal, 126; normal, 15; stationary-state, 138
Diversion: 9, 174, 175, 181, 190; tunnels, 46
Dorfman, R., 1n, 15n, 154n
Drainage areas: ratios, 25; reservoir, 159
Drawdown, 81
Dump power. See Energy, Power
Dumps, memory, 152
Duration, 20, 21, 127, 151; of flooding, 71
Dynamic analysis, 83, 85, 87

Eckstein, O., 68n, 69n, 71n
Economic consequences of system, 83–87
Economic life, 83
Economic loss: 42, 55; functions, 77–82
Economies, scale, 51
Efficiencies, generator, 37
Eigenvalues, 25
Eigenvectors, 18, 25
Energy, 62–65, 105, 133, 186; benefits, 62–65; deficit, 78–79, 97, 105, 110, 123, 133, 134, 163, 187; dump, 105, 134; dump benefits, 186; electric, 9, 96; excess, 185, 187, 188; loss function, 79; peaking, 63; requirement, 175; target, 34, 186, 190; test, 111; total, 105; value, 62–65
Engineering, civil, 194
Equation, differential, 194
Erosion, 6
Estimates: demand, 50; standard errors of, 155
Evaporation, 6, 7
Evapotranspiration, 13
Excess, 186; energy, 187, 188; water-supply, 187
External alternative, 60, 61

Facilities: 52; maintenance, 52; operation, 52; physical, 29; replacement, 52
Factor: discount, 136; hedging, 130; plant capacity, 34
Fair, G. M., 15n, 75n, 154n

Federal Power Commission, 46n, 53, 63, 65n
Field, well, 13
Fiering, M. B., 15n, 19n
Fish, 7, 77
Fitting, spline curve, 139
Flexibility, 196
Flood: damage–discharge function, 72; damage zones, 72; flows, 70; losses, 71; plain, 72; stage, 71; warning systems, 72
Flood-control, 70–73, 169; benefits, 70–73
Flood-damage prevention, 82
Flood-damages, 165
Flood proofing, 72
Flood storage allowance, 33, 99, 125
Floods: 34; type 1, 130; type 2, 130
Flow: base, 21; critical low, 2; effective power, 105, 176; excess, 100; flood, 20, 70; gamma-distributed, 96; historical, 96, 154; inevitable, 98, 174; intermediate, 106; log-normally distributed, 96; minimal channel, 36; minimal stream, 96; negative, 156; normally distributed, 96; residual, 13; synthetic, 156; target, 174; three-hourly flood, 27; unregulated, 106; unregulated peak, 23; velocity, 71
Fluctuations, diurnal, 154
Flux, radioactivity, 75
Forrester, J. W., 82n
FORTRAN, 3, 19, 193
Functions, 36, 42, 51; benefit, 42; cost, 42; cost-capacity, 43; discharge–damage, 134; economic-loss, 42, 77; long-run benefit, 42; loss, 134; objective, 157; recreation capacity, 50; storage capacity, 50; storage-yield, 198; unit cost, 46

Gaps, 25
Gas turbine, 64
Generator: flood, 20; monthly operational hydrology, 15; random number, 93; streamflow, 154
Geology, 7
Geyer, J. C., 75n
Gilchrist: method, 125; modified method, 129, 131
Ground-water: 13; aquifer, 5; conjunctive use of, 13; pumping, 9; relationships, 5

Hanson, R. J., 40n
Hardness, 75

Hazard, flood, 7
Head: average, 39; capacity functions, 39; contents curves, 89; fixed factors of, 37; maximum, 37; pumping, 39; rated, 188
Hoggatt, A. C., 158n
Horizon, economic-time, 90
Hufschmidt, M. M., 5n, 15n, 17n, 30n, 40n, 43n, 56n, 69n, 77n, 81n, 86n, 154n, 156n, 158n, 159n, 197n
Hydroelectric energy, 153
Hydroelectric power facilities, 45
Hydroelectric power plants, 9
Hydrograph, 21; flood, 129; synthetic flood, 14
Hydrologic data, 24
Hydrology: 1, 7, 194; generators, 95; input, 137; operational generator, 13, 14, 94; recorded flows, 159; synthetic streamflow traces, 14, 159
Hydrologic record, actual, 170
Hydrologic traces, 168

IBM 7094, 15, 25, 89, 193, 195
Improvements, channel, 9
Inconsistency, 156; internal, 152, 153
Index, quality, 76
Indus River system, 13
Initialization, 133, 173
Inputs, resource, 42
Integer, random, 126
Interest rate, 4, 188
Interpolation, 23
Invariant: 29, 89; physical functions, 30
Inventory, 197
Investment, constant unit cost of, 51
Iron, 75
Irrigation, 67–69, 81; benefits, 68; benefit function, 69; loss function, 81
Iteration, 175

Job, 89, 133
Jonker, R., 3n
Jordan Creek, 25–28, 72

Kates, R., 71n, 72n
Kendall, M. G., 18n, 156n
Key-punching, 25
Kneese, A. V., 60n, 75n, 76n, 82n
Knetsch, J. L., 67n
Kohler, M., 27n
Krutilla, J. V., 56n

Lag one, 155
Lehigh area, power requirements, 62
Lehigh River system: 3, 4, 19, 41, 43,

73, 183; major design variables, 46, 68; power plants, 46; reservoirs, 52

Lehigh system design, 168–170

Levees, 9

Level: lower constraint, 185; second constraint, 183; upper constraint, 185; dead-storage, 176

Lewis, D. J., 3n

Lewis, D. S., 30n

Limbs: falling, 21, 151; rising, 21, 128, 151

Lines, transmission, 48

Linsley, R. K., 27n

Loops, 180

Loss functions. *See* Economic loss

Losses, flood, 71–73

Maass, Arthur, 15n, 17n, 30n, 40n, 43n, 56n, 69n, 77n, 81n, 86n, 154n, 156n, 158n, 159n

Mahoning reservoir, 12, 13n, 96

MAIN subroutine, 93, 125, 129, 131, 133, 134, 135, 136, 196

Marginal analysis, 159

Marginal price, 60

Marglin, S., 15n, 154n

Margolis, J., 56n

Markov: model, 15; process, 155

Markovian population, 155

Matrix, correlation, 18

Mean, 157

Measure, development, 9, 43, 45

Merewitz, L., 67n

Mineralization, 6

Missouri River, 20n, 77

Mnemonics, 93

Mode, 153 ; deterministic, 153; octal, 151; stochastic, 153

Model: mathematical, 15; physical, 2

Moments, 17, 154, 155, 156, 157

Montague, 174, 175, 181, 190

Months, standard, 24

National Park Service, 48, 51n, 53, 67

Navigation, 7, 77

New Jersey, 175, 183

New York, 9; diversions to, 183; water supply network, 174

Normal, multivariate, 155

Numbers, random, 127, 151

Operation: of completed systems, 199; low-flow, 195

Operation, maintenance and replacement (OMR) costs. *See* Costs

Operations research, 1

Opportunity costs, 61

Outdoor Recreation Resources Review Commission, 48n, 80n

Output, assigned, 42; target, 3, 34, 55, 96, 97

Oxygen, dissolved, 75

Parameters, 29; hydrologic, 90

Paulhus, J., 27n

Payoff, economic, 42

Peak: daily, 20; flood, 125, 174; monthly flood, 171

Penstocks, 36, 46; capacity, 36

Performance, physical, 42

Period: critical, 154; demand, 85–87, 90, 133, 136, 138, 139, 174; of economic analysis, 83, 159

Periodograms, 155

Phenol, 75

Philadelphia, 9, 175, 183, 187, 188, 190

Plan formulation, 5

Planned output. *See* Target output

Planning, detailed, 198

Plant, power, 176

Pohopoco Creek, 25–28, 72

Points, use of, 175

Policy: basic, 96; operating, 14, 171; optimal operating, 40; parameters, 29

Polynomial, 134, 139; coefficients, 190; loss function, 134

Pondage, 45

Population, 16; mean, 16; standard deviation, 16

Port Jervis, 187

Potomac basin report, 5

Power: dump, 55; firm, 55; loss functions, 78, 79; plant capacity factor, 64, 65; run-of-the-river, 45; value of, 62; *see also* Energy

Power plant capacity, 159

President's Water Resources Council, 50n

Priorities, 41

Probabilities, stationary state, 42

Procedure, operating, 4, 33

Process, planning, 9

Products, cross, 94

Program, 196; binary object, 89; executive, 171, 174

Programmer, 193, 194

Programming, 194

Project design, detailed, 198

Projected water flow, requirements for, 35

Prototype, 194

Random sample, 158, 160, 170

Reading, 175, 183, 184, 187, 188, 190

Reclamation, U.S. Bureau of, 2
Reconnaissance, 197
Record, historical, 14; actual hydrologic, 170
Recreation: 7, 9, 48, 79–81, 169; attendance, 65–67, 80, 188; benefits, 135; capacity, 52, 66; constraint, 97, 134, 184; constraint levels, 41, 159, 165, 190; deficits, 188; demand, 66; development, 50; facilities, 50, 66; loss function, 80; losses, 134, 187; OMR costs for, 53; output, 66; pool level, 80; pool storage for, 34; prime season, 80; services, 65; specialists, 48; cost of facilities, 51, 52
Regression: 125, 126, 127; coefficient, 16, 94; equations, 155; linear model, 16
Releases, additional, 97; basic, 99, 107, 176, 181, 190; supplementary, 98, 99, 100, 107, 175, 176; trial, 185
Reservoirs: admissible, 124; area, 51; capacity, 51; refill period, 36; shoreline topography, 81
Resource savings, 60
Return, expected, 156
Riegelsville, 187
Rippl analysis, 198
Risk, aversion to, 156, 157
Routine: executive, 93, 152, 173, 189, 192; main, 89, 91
Routing, 24; flood, 153; sequence, 125
Rule curves, 34n
Rule, space, 176, 182, 183, 185
Run-of-river power, 45
Runs, 90, 151; discounted, 136, 138, 168, 188; undiscounted, 135, 136, 138, 168, 188

Salinity, 13
Salinization, 6
Sample: random, 158, 169, 170; systematic, 169, 170
Satellite, 17
Schedules, development, 89
Schuylkill River, 175, 183, 184, 187
Screening, preliminary, 5, 10, 197
Sedimentation, 7
Sensitivity, 23; analysis of, 165
Sequence, 2; long hydrologic, 3; routing, 125
Sequential analysis, 160
Sequential process, 159
Shoemaker, L. A., 3n, 30n
Shortage, 99
Siltation, 6

Simulation, 1, 2, 159, 168; advanced, 3; analog, 1; conventional, 2; digital, 1; period, 83–87, 170; run, 34, 83–87, 168, 170
Single factor method, 159
Skewness, 16, 151
Sobel, M. J., 82n
Soils, 7
Solids, dissolved, 75
Specification: automatic, 195; random, 195; systematic, 195
Spills, 24, 97
Stage-discharge function, 70
Standard project flood, 34n
State, steady, 42
Static analysis, 83, 84
Stations: key, 17; gaging, 189
Statistics, 194
Steiner, P. O., 56n
Storage capacity, range of, 158
Strategy, sampling, 158
Streamflows, 168
Stuart, A., 156n
Studies: 2, 89, 133, 139; operation, 2; simulation, 2
Subroutines
    BASIC, 98, 173, 174, 181, 192
    BENACM, 133, 174, 186, 191
    BENACY, 133, 135, 174, 187, 188, 191
    BENDYN, 133, 136, 138, 152, 174, 188, 191
    BOX, 175, 176, 181, 185, 190, 191
    COST, 133, 137, 174, 188, 191
    DIVERT, 98, 110
    FAP, 191
    FGEN, 125, 129, 130, 174, 190, 192
    FSPACE, 125, 130–133
    GM, 139, 191
    HYDRO, 125, 129
    MONT, 173, 174, 181, 191
    POWER, 98, 152, 153, 173, 175, 184, 191, 192
    PYFT, 191
    RANDM, 151
    READ1, 93, 152, 173, 174, 189
    READ2, 93, 152
    ROUTER, 125, 129, 130, 132, 133, 152
    SETUP, 93
    SETUPB, 93, 133, 173, 186, 191
    SHARE, 191
    SPACE, 98, 110, 132, 133, 152, 175–177, 179, 185, 191
    SUPPOW, 98, 152
    SYNHYD, 94, 151
    WATER, 98, 173, 175, 183, 192

WRITE1, 189
WRITE2, 174, 189
Supply, water, 5
Surcharge, 109, 123, 124
Switchyards, 48
Synthetic traces of hydrology, 159, 165, 170. *See also* Hydrology
Systematic analysis, 159
Systematic sample, 169, 170
Systems: analysis, 1, 197; components, 29; outputs, 29; performance, 42; monitor, 189

Tannery, 25–28; 96
Target, 77, 184; energy, 34, 186, 190; output, 54, 55, 77, 159, 163; water supply, 57, 186
Technique, spline, 95
Temperature, 75
Tennessee Valley Authority, 80n
Thermal power, 62–65
Thomann, R. V., 82n
Thomas, H. A., Jr., 13n, 15n, 154n
Thomson, J., 3n
Time: concentration, 14; dependence, 155; lag, 126; streams of benefits, 168; turn-around, 195
Time-interval, characteristic, 153
Time-of-peak, 20, 126, 151
Time-of-travel, 126
Tobyhanna reservoir, 11, 13n, 96
Tocks Island, 175
Tolerance, 117, 175, 185
Topography, 7
Traces: synthetic flow, 154; synthetic hydrology, 159–165; synthetic stream-flow, 14. *See also* Hydrology
Transforms, 155; inverse linear, 18; linear, 96; logarithmic, 20, 95, 126, 127, 156
Treatment, waste, 9
Trenton, 187
Trexler reservoir, 12, 13n, 96
Turbidity, 75
Turbine, 37; capacity, 110
TVA system, 1; *see also* Tennessee Valley Authority

Undiscounted run, 135, 136, 138, 168, 188

United Nations Economic Commission for Asia and the Far East, 7
United States Army Corps of Engineers, 2n, 3n, 5n, 52, 61, 67, 169
United States Bureau of Reclamation, 68n
United States Geological Survey, 20n, 80n
United States Supreme Court, 174, 175
UNIVAC 1, 193
Use, land, 7

Validation, 151
Values: nominal, 135; present, 139, 156, 188
Variable, 89; head power plant, 188; run-control, 90
Variance, 157
Variate, dependent, 17
Vector, 33, 34
Visitor-day, annual, 50; attendance, 50, 65

Walnutport, 14, 20, 23–28, 72, 96, 128–132
Warning, flood, 10, 72
Water: spreading, 9; surface, 7; transmission, 9; value of, 68
Water quality: 7, 9, 75–77; benefits, 76; control, 10; improvement, 75; loss function, 82; management, 82, 195
Water-resource planning, 197
Water-resource systems, 1; operation of, 52
Water-saving measures, 59
Water supplies: 7, 96, 97, 169, 190; benefits, 135; commercial, 7; deficits, 134; domestic, 7; industrial, 7; target, 34, 77
Water supply: 5; demand, 78; output, 57; loss functions, 77, 78
Waterlogging, 13
Weaver, R. M., 43n
Wedge, flood, 128
West Pakistan, 13
White G. F., 71, 72
Wildlife, 7, 77
Willingness to pay, 56–61, 66–67, 76

Zoning, flood-plain, 10